PROVING PROGRAMS CORRECT

PROVING PROGRAMS CORRECT

ROBERT B. ANDERSON

University of Houston

JOHN WILEY & SONS
New York   Chichester   Brisbane   Toronto

Library of Congress Cataloging in Publication Data

Anderson, Robert Brockett, 1941-
   Proving programs correct.

   Bibliography: p.
   Includes index.
   1. Computer programs—Testing. 2. Debugging in
computer science.   I. Title.
QA76.6.A47   001.6'425   78-9321
ISBN 0-471-03395-2

Printed in the United States of America
10 9 8 7 6 5 4 3 2

PREFACE

The purpose of this book is to explain and illustrate some basic techniques for proving computer programs correct. A large research effort has been devoted to this topic in recent years. Much of this research is aimed at formalizing and ultimately mechanizing such proofs. Our emphasis, however, is on rather informal correctness proofs of the type programmers can employ in trying to systematically convince themselves of their program's correctness. Of course, we are well aware that informal correctness proofs can easily contain errors and are no panacea for preventing or discovering all programming errors. Nevertheless, we do believe that such informal correctness proofs provide programmers with a more systematic means of desk checking their programs. We also think that the basic techniques used in correctness proofs give additional insights into the most basic programming constructs, looping, and recursion. For these reasons we believe that all programmers should be taught the basic techniques for proving programs correct.

The only prerequisites for understanding this book are programming experience in a high-level programming language and some slight exposure to mathematical proofs. Almost no specific mathematical knowledge is required. Chapter 1 provides a thorough introduction to mathematical induction, which is the main mathematical proof technique that underlies correctness proofs.

Chapter 2 examines the method of inductive assertions, which is the most commonly used technique in correctness proofs for iterative programs. It contains the most basic material. Chapter 3 illustrates further the method of inductive assertions for FORTRAN and

PL/I programs. It also briefly introduces the idea of verification rules and their equivalence with the method of inductive assertions. In Chapter 4 we deal with the method of structural induction, which is the most commonly used technique for proving the correctness of recursive programs. This technique is also shown to be useful in proving the correctness of iterative programs that are basically carrying out recursive processes. Chapter 5 is a very brief introduction to some of the current research related to proving program correctness. We have also supplied a fairly extensive bibliography as an aid to the reader who is interested in pursuing this topic.

This book can be used as a supplementary text for an undergraduate or first-year graduate course on the theory of computation. It can also be used as a supplementary text in a second course on programming emphasizing such topics as programming style and program correctness. Since it is sufficiently self-explanatory, it can also be used for self-study by any one with a slight familiarity with mathematical proofs and a background in programming.

Robert B. Anderson

CONTENTS

CHAPTER IV PROVING THE CORRECTNESS OF
            RECURSIVE PROGRAMS

CHAPTER V CURRENT RESEARCH RELATED TO
           PROVING PROGRAM CORRECTNESS

CHAPTER ONE

MATHEMATICAL INDUCTION

1.1 INTRODUCTION

Mathematical induction is a standard method of proof in mathematics. Although not always explicitly stated, it is the underlying technique of all correctness proofs for computer programs. This chapter is intended to thoroughly familiarize the reader with this fundamental method of proof.

Mathematical induction is usually stated as a method of proving statements about the positive integers. In the next section we state and illustrate the most elementary version of this method. In Section 1.3 we give a slightly stronger version of it, and in Section 1.4 we give a generalization of the method that is applicable to proving statements about any well-ordered set rather than just the positive integers. Only the material in Section 1.2 is necessary for most of the book. Therefore, you may prefer to skip Sections 1.3 and 1.4 and only return to them later if needed. Section 1.4 is more abstract than Sections 1.2 and 1.3 and should be skipped by the reader who lacks "mathematical maturity."

1.2 SIMPLE INDUCTION

THE SIMPLE INDUCTION PRINCIPLE

Suppose $S(n)$ is some statement about the integer n and we wish to prove that $S(n)$ is true for all positive integers n. The method of simple induction states that in order to prove this we only need to:
   (i)   Prove that $S(1)$ is true.
   (ii) Prove (for all positive integers n) that if $S(n)$ is true then $S(n + 1)$ is also true.

1

The fact that these two statements together do show that S (n) is true for all positive integers is intuitively obvious (although, in an axiomatic treatment of the integers, some form of this principle would have to be assumed as an axiom). From (i), we know that S(1) is true. From (ii) we know that if S(1) is true then S(2) is also true. But S(1) is true and hence S(2) must also be true. From (ii) we also know that if S(2) is true then S(3) is also true. Thus, since we know that S(2) is true, it follows that S(3) is also true, and so on. Hence, intuitively we see that (i) and (ii) together show that S(1), S(2), S(3),..., S (n),... are all true.

We now give several examples of the use of a simple induction.

EXAMPLE 1.2.1

We wish to prove for all positive integers n that the sum of the first n positive integers is equal to n $\cdot$ (n + 1)/2. In other words, for all positive integers n, 1+2+...+n = n$\cdot$(n + 1)/2. To prove this by simple induction, we only need to prove:

(i)   The sum of the first 1 positive integers is equal to 1$\cdot$(1+1)/2, that is, 1 = 1$\cdot$(1+1)/2. This is obviously true.

(ii)   If the sum of the first n positive integers equals n$\cdot$(n+1)/2, then the sum of the first n+1 positive integers equals (n+1)$\cdot$[(n+1)+1]/2. Thus we may assume that 1+2+$\cdots$+n=n$\cdot$(n+1)/2 is true. This is called the induction hypothesis, and we must try to prove that it follows from this that
1+2+$\cdots$+n+(n+1) = (n+1)$\cdot$[(n+1)+1]/2 is also true.

To prove this note that

$$1+2+\cdots+n+(n+1) = (1+2+\cdots n)+(n+1)$$

$$= [n\cdot(n+1)/2]+(n+1) \quad \text{by the induction}$$

$$= [(n^2+n)/2]+(n+1) \quad \text{hypothesis}$$

$$= [(n^2+n)/2]+[(2n+2)/2]$$

$$= (n^2+3n+2)/2$$

$$= (n+1) \cdot (n+2)/2$$

$$= (n+1) \cdot [(n+1)+1]/2$$

This concludes the proof of part (ii). Since (i) and (ii) have both been proven, simple induction justifies the claim that for all positive integers n, $1+2+\cdots+n = n \cdot (n+1)/2$.

THE MODIFIED SIMPLE INDUCTION PRINCIPLE

Sometimes we wish to prove that a statement $S(n)$ is true for all integers $n \geq n_0$. Simple induction can be trivially modified to show this as follows. In order to prove that $S(n)$ is true for all integers $n \geq n_0$ we only need to:

(i)   Prove that $S(n_0)$ is true.
(ii) Prove (for all integers $n \geq n_0$) that if $S(n)$ is true, then $S(n+1)$ is also true.

In particular, if we wish to prove that some statement $S(n)$ is true for all nonnegative integers (i.e., $n \geq 0$), we only need to:

(i)   Prove that $S(0)$ is true.
(ii) Prove that (for all nonnegative integers n) if $S(n)$ is true then $S(n+1)$ is also true.

EXAMPLE 1.2.2

For all nonnegative integers n, we wish to prove that $2^0+2^1+2^2+\cdots+2^n = 2^{n+1} - 1$. In order to prove this by simple induction, do the following.

(i)   Prove that $2^0 = 2^{0+1}-1$. But this is obvious, since $2^0 = 1 = 2^{0+1}-1$

$$= 2^1-1$$

$$= 2-1$$

$$= 1$$

(ii) Prove that (for all nonnegative integers n) if

$$2^0+2^1+2^2+\cdots+2^n = 2^{n+1}-1 \text{ is true, then}$$

$$2^0+2^1+2^2+\cdots+2^n+2^{n+1} = 2^{(n+1)+1}-1 \text{ is also true.}$$

The statement $2^0+2^1+2^2+\cdots+2^n = 2^{n+1}-1$ is called the induction hypothesis. To prove (ii) note that

$$2^0+2^1+2^2+\cdots+2^n+2^{n+1} = (2^0+2^1+2^2+\cdots+2^n)+2^{n+1}$$

$$= (2^{n+1}-1)+2^{n+1} \text{ by the induction hypothesis}$$

$$= (2^{n+1}+2^{n+1})-1$$

$$= (2\cdot2^{n+1})-1$$

$$= 2^{n+2}-1$$

$$= 2^{(n+1)+1}-1$$

We sometimes wish to prove that a statement $S(n)$ is true for all integers n such that $n_0 \le n \le m_0$. Since there are only a finite number of integers between n_0 and m_0, we may be able to prove $S(n)$ is true for all of these by merely checking all of the different cases. However, it is often easier and sometimes necessary (e.g., when we don't know specific values for n_0 or m_0) to prove $S(n)$ by induction. In this situation there are two versions of simple induction that one can try to use to show that $S(n)$ is true for all $n_0 \le n \le m_0$:

SIMPLE UPWARD INDUCTION
   (i)   Prove that $S(n_0)$ is true.
   (ii)   Prove (for all integers $n_0 \le n \le m_0-1$) that if $S(n)$ is true then $S(n+1)$ is also true.

SIMPLE DOWNWARD INDUCTION
   (i)   Prove that $S(m_0)$ is true.
   (ii)   Prove (for all integers $n_0+1 \le n \le m_0$ that if $S(n)$ is true then $S(n-1)$ is also true.
   The student should be able to see that intuitively each of these is sufficient to prove that $S(n)$ is true for all $n_0 \le n \le m_0$.

PROVING STATEMENTS ABOUT COMPUTER PROGRAMS
    Sometimes it is ambiguous whether we are trying to prove that $S(n)$ is true for all n so that $n_0 \leq n \leq m_0$ or $n_0 \leq n$. In such situations we can frequently prove the result without knowing which of the two cases is involved. For example, in proving program correctness, we sometimes want to prove that a statement S is true each time execution reaches a particular point in the program. We might try to prove this by induction on n the number of times that execution has reached the point. But we may not know exactly how many times execution will reach this point - this may depend on what data is used when the program is executed. Execution may reach the point some finite number of times m_0, or it may reach the point an infinite number of times if the program fails to terminate. Thus we may be trying to prove that $S(n)$ is true for all n so that $1 \leq n \leq m_0$ or $1 \leq n$. Nevertheless, we may be able to prove the result without knowing which of the two possibilities is in fact the case. If we can prove the following, then we are justified in claiming that $S(n)$ is true each time execution reaches the point:
    (i) $S(1)$ is true (i.e., S is true the first time execution reaches the point).
    (ii)   If $S(n)$ is true (i.e., S is true the nth time execution reaches the point) and execution returns to the point for an $n+1^{th}$ time, then $S(n+1)$ is also true (i.e., S is true the $n+1^{th}$ time execution reaches the point)
If execution only reaches the point m_0 times, the only values of n for which the hypothesis of (ii) can possibly be true -- those values of n for which execution will return to the point for an $n+1^{th}$ time -- are all those values of n such that $1 \leq n \leq m_0-1$. On the other hand, if execution reaches the point an infinite number of times, the values of n for which the hypothesis of (ii) could be true are all those values of n such that $1 \leq n$. Thus if we can prove (i) and (ii) we will have proved by simple upward induction or simple induction that $S(n)$ is true for all the relevant values of n, regardless of which of the two possibilities is the case.

EXERCISES

1. Prove that for all positive integers n,

$$\frac{1}{(1)\cdot(2)} + \frac{1}{(2)\cdot(3)} + \cdots + \frac{1}{(n)\cdot(n+1)} = \frac{n}{n+1}$$

2. Prove that for all nonnegative integers n

$$3^0 + 3^1 + 3^2 + \cdots + 3^n = \frac{3^{n+1}-1}{2}$$

3. Prove that for all positive integers n,

$$1^3 + 2^3 + \cdots + n^3 = \frac{n^2 \cdot (n+1)^2}{4}$$

Note that this together with Example 1.2.1 proves the remarkable fact that

$$1^3 + 2^3 + \cdots + n^3 = (1+2+\cdots+n)^2.$$

4.

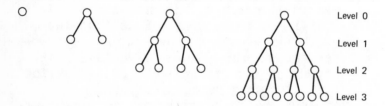

The above graphs are examples of complete binary trees of levels 0, 1, 2, and 3. A complete binary tree of level n is a graph like the above in which all nodes except those on level n have two branches coming out of them. The nodes at level n that do not have any branches coming out of them are called the tip or leaf nodes of the tree. Prove by induction on the level n that the number of tip nodes in a complete binary tree of level n is 2^n. Find a formula for the total number of nodes (both tip and nontip nodes) in such a tree and prove the formula by induction.

5.

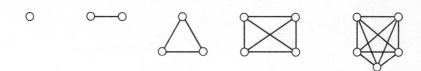

The above graphs are examples of complete graphs
containing 1, 2, 3, 4, and 5 nodes.   A complete
graph on n nodes is a graph like the above, which
contains n nodes and has one link or branch con-
necting each pair of nodes in the graph.   Figure
out a formula for the number of branches or links
that occur in a complete graph on n nodes and
prove the formula by induction on n.

6.   Find the error in the following proposed proof.   We
wish to prove that

$$\frac{1}{1\cdot2} + \frac{1}{2\cdot3} + \cdots + \frac{1}{(n-1)\cdot(n)} = \frac{3n-2}{2n}$$

for all positive integers n.   The proof is by induction on n.
(i)   For n = 1, the formula is true for

$$\frac{1}{1\cdot2} = \frac{3\cdot1-2}{2\cdot1} = \frac{3-2}{2} = \frac{1}{2}$$

(ii)   Suppose the formula is true for n, that is,

$$\frac{1}{1\cdot2} + \frac{1}{2\cdot3} + \cdots + \frac{1}{(n-1)\cdot(n)} = \frac{3n-2}{2n}$$

then note that

$$\frac{1}{1\cdot2} + \frac{1}{2\cdot3} + \cdots + \frac{1}{(n-1)\cdot(n)} + \frac{1}{n(n+1)}$$

$$= \frac{1}{1\cdot2} + \frac{1}{2\cdot3} + \cdots + \frac{1}{(n-1)\cdot(n)} + \frac{1}{n(n+1)}$$

$$= \frac{3n-2}{2n} + \frac{1}{n(n+1)} \qquad \text{by the induction hypothesis}$$

$$= \frac{(3n-2)(n+1)}{(2n)(n+1)} + \frac{2}{(2n)(n+1)}$$

$$= \frac{3n^2 + n - 2 + 2}{2n(n+1)}$$

$$= \frac{3n^2 + n}{2n(n+1)}$$

$$= \frac{n(3n+1)}{2n(n+1)}$$

$$= \frac{3n+1}{2(n+1)}$$

$$= \frac{3(n+1)-2}{2(n+1)}$$

Thus it is true for n+1 also.
Although the proof appears to be valid it must be incorrect, since when n = 4, we get

$$\frac{1}{1\cdot2} + \frac{1}{2\cdot3} + \frac{1}{3\cdot4} = \frac{1}{2} + \frac{1}{6} + \frac{1}{12} = \frac{9}{12} = \frac{3}{4}$$

But $\frac{3n-2}{2n} = \frac{3\cdot4-2}{2\cdot4} = \frac{10}{8} \neq \frac{3}{4}$

7. Find the error in the following proposed proof. We wish to prove that any collection of marbles contains only marbles of the same color. The proof will be by induction on the number, n, of marbles in the collection.

(i)   For n = 1 it is obvious, since any collection of marbles that contains only one marble obviously contains only marbles of the same color.

(ii) Suppose the statement is true for any collection of n marbles. Let us show that it is then also true for any collection of n+1 marbles.

Suppose we picture a collection of n+1 marbles as

$$
\begin{matrix}
0 & 0 & . & . & . & 0 & 0 \\
1 & 2 & & & & n & n+1
\end{matrix}
$$

If we remove the n+1st marble from this collection, we are left with a collection of n marbles:

$$
\begin{matrix}
0 & 0 & . & . & . & 0 \\
1 & 2 & & & & n
\end{matrix}
$$

By the induction hypothesis all the marbles in this collection must be of the same color. Now suppose that we instead remove the first marble from the collection. Then we are left with the collection:

$$
\begin{matrix}
0 & 0 & . & . & . & 0 & 0 \\
2 & 3 & & & & n & n+1
\end{matrix}
$$

But this collection also contains n marbles and hence, by the induction hypothesis, all the marbles in this collection must also be of the same color. This implies that all n+1 marbles are of the same color, since we know that marbles

$$
\begin{matrix}
0 & 0 & . & . & . & 0 \\
1 & 2 & & & & n
\end{matrix}
$$

are all of the same color and the n+1st marble is also of the same color as marble n (in fact, it is not only the same color as marble n: it is the same color as marbles 2, 3, ..., n.) Thus all n+1 marbles are of the same color.

1.3   A STRONGER VERSION OF MATHEMATICAL INDUCTION

Sometimes a slightly stronger version of the induction method is needed to prove some statement about the integers. This slightly stronger version is the following.

THE STRONG INDUCTION PRINCIPLE

Suppose S(n) is some statement about the integer n and we wish to prove that S(n) is true for all positive integers n. In order to prove this we only need to:

  (i)   Prove that S(1) is true.
  (ii) Prove (for all positive integers n) that if S(1), S(2), ..., S(n) are all true, then S(n+1) is also true.

Note that this stronger version of induction is identical to simple induction, except that in proving (ii) we get to assume as the induction hypothesis that all of the statements S(1), S(2), ..., S(n) are true rather than simply that S(n) is true. From this stronger induction hypothesis, we still need only to show that S(n+1) is true.

As with simple induction, it is intuitively clear that (i) and (ii) together imply that S(n) is true for all positive integers n. By (i) we know that S(1) is true. From (ii) we know that if S(1) is true, then S(2) is also true and hence, since S(1) is known to be true, then S(2) must also be true. But then, since S(1) is known to be true and S(2) is also known to be true, (ii) would imply that S(3) is also true. And, since S(1), S(2), and S(3) are all known to be true, (ii) would imply that S(4) is also true, etc.

We now give several examples where this stronger version of induction is useful.

EXAMPLE   1.3.1

A positive integer is called a prime number if the only positive integers that divide it without remainder are 1 and itself. We wish to prove that every positive integer n can be expressed as the product of (one or more) prime numbers. The proof is by strong induction on n.

  (i)   If n = 1, then it is itself a prime number and hence can be expressed as the product of (one) prime number(s).
  (ii) Suppose that each of the numbers 1, 2, ...,n can be expressed as the product of prime numbers. We need to show that n+1 can also

be expressed as the product of prime numbers. If n+1 is itself a prime number, then obviously it can be expressed as the product of (one) prime number(s). If n+1 is not a prime number then there is some positive integer a such that 1<a<n+1 and a divides n+1 without remainder. In other words,

$$\frac{(n+1)}{a} = b \text{ or } n+1 = a \cdot b.$$

But each of the integer numbers a, b is $\leq$ n. Thus, by the induction hypothesis, both a and b can be expressed as the product of prime numbers. But then n+1 can obviously be expressed as the product of these prime numbers, since n+1 = a $\cdot$ b.

Note that we really need the stronger version of induction for the above proof. All we know is that a and b are both $\leq$ n and, therefore, to be able to apply the induction hypothesis to them, we need to know that each of the positive integers 1, 2, ..., n can be expressed as a product of primes. Just assuming that n could be expressed as a product of primes would not suffice.

EXAMPLE   1.3.2

This example deals with a sequence of numbers known as the Fibonacci numbers. This sequence is $f_0 = 0$, $f_1 = 1$, $f_2 = 1$, $f_3 = 2$, $f_4 = 3$, $f_5 = 5$, $f_6 = 8, \ldots$ where the n+1th Fibonacci number f_{n+1} is determined by $f_{n+1} = f_n + f_{n-1}$ (if $n \geq 1$). Let $\alpha = (1 + \sqrt{5})/2$. We wish to prove that for every nonnegative integer n, $f_n \leq \alpha^{n-1}$. The proof will be by strong induction on n. Since we are trying to prove a statement about the nonnegative integers rather than the positive integers, we use an obvious modification of the method (see Exercise 1 at the end of this section).

(i) For $n = 0$ we need to show that $f_0 \leq \alpha^{0-1}$.
but this is true, since $f_0 = 0 \leq \dfrac{2}{(1+\sqrt{5})} = \alpha^{-1}$.
We also need to make a special case out of $n = 1$, which is $f_1 = 1 \leq 1 = \alpha^0 = \alpha^{1-1}$.

(ii) Suppose $f_m \leq \alpha^{m-1}$ is true for all nonnegative
integers $m = 0, 1, \ldots, n$. We need to show
that $f_{n+1} = \alpha^{(n+1)-1}$ is also true. But the
induction hypothesis tells us that $f_n \leq \alpha^{n-1}$
and $f_{n-1} \leq \alpha^{(n-1)-1}$. Therefore

$$f_{n+1} = f_n + f_{n-1} \leq \alpha^{n-1} + \alpha^{n-2} = \alpha^{n-2}(\alpha + 1).$$

But note that

$$\alpha^2 = (\tfrac{1+\sqrt{5}}{2})^2$$

$$= \frac{1+2\sqrt{5}+5}{4}$$

$$= \frac{6+2\sqrt{5}}{4}$$

$$= \frac{3+\sqrt{5}}{2}$$

$$= \frac{1+\sqrt{5}}{2} + 1$$

$$= \alpha + 1$$

Indeed, α was chosen specifically because
$\alpha + 1 = \alpha^2$. Therefore we have

$$f_{n+1} = f_n + f_{n-1} \leq \alpha^{n-2}(\alpha + 1)$$

$$\leq \alpha^{n-2}(\alpha^2)$$

$$\leq \alpha^n$$

$$\leq \alpha^{(n+1)-1}$$

This completes the proof. Notice that we needed to know that both f_n and f_{n-1} satisfied the induction hypothesis in order to carry out the proof. Only knowing that f_n did would not suffice. Thus we really need the stronger version of induction in order to carry out this proof. Also notice that for this particular example, we needed to prove both that $f_0 \leq \alpha^0$ and $f_1 \leq \alpha^1$; we cannot express f_1 as $= f_0 + f_{-1}$, since there is no f_{-1}.

EXERCISES

1. Modify the induction method given in this section for proving that a statement $S(n)$ is true for all integers $n \geq n_0$ (rather than for all positive integers).

2. Prove by (simple) induction that $f_0 + f_1 + \cdots + f_n = f_{n+2} - 1$ for all nonnegative integers n.

3. Prove by (simple) induction that for all positive integers n, $f_2 + f_4 + f_6 + \cdots + f_{2 \cdot n} = f_{2n+1} - 1$.

4. Prove by (simple) induction that for all nonnegative integers n, $f_0^2 + f_1^2 + \cdots + f_n^2 = f_n \cdot f_{n+1}$.

5. Prove by (strong) induction that for all positive integers n, $\alpha^{n-2} \leq f_n$, where $\alpha = \frac{(1+\sqrt{5})}{2}$.

6. Prove by (strong) induction that for all nonnegative integers n, $f_n \leq (\frac{7}{4})^{n-1}$

7. Find the error in the following proposed proof. We wish to prove that $a^{n-1} = 1$ for all positive integers n. We will prove this by (strong) induction on n.
    (i) For n = 1 we have $a^{n-1} = a^{1-1} = a^0 = 1$.

(ii)   Suppose the statement is true for 1, 2, 3, ..., n, that is, $a^0 = 1$, $a^1 = 1$, $a^2 = 1$, ..., $a^{n-1} = 1$.   We wish to show then that $a^{(n+1)-1} = 1$.   To do this, note that

$$a^{(n+1)-1} = a^n = a^1 \cdot a^{n-1}$$

$$= 1 \cdot 1 \quad \text{by the induction hypothesis}$$

$$= 1$$

8.   Formulate two versions of strong induction that can be used to try to prove that $S(n)$ is true for all $n_0 \leq n \leq m_0$.   We will refer to these as strong, upward induction and strong, downward induction.   See the discussion at the end of Section 1.2 on the corresponding versions of simple induction.

1.4   GENERALIZED INDUCTION

It is possible to generalize the method of mathematical induction so that it can be applied not only to proofs about the set of positive integers but to proofs about more general sets of objects.   In order to give this more general principle of induction, we need to generalize the basic structure of the positive integers.

DEFINITION 1.4.1
   A binary relation $<$ on a set X is said to be a well ordering (or the set X is said to be well ordered by $<$) provided that $<$ has the following properties:
   (i)   Given x, y, z in X, if $x < y$ and $y < z$, then $x < z$.
   (ii)   Given x, y in X, exactly one of the following three possibilities is true: either $x < y$ or $y < x$ or $x = y$.
   (iii)   If A is any nonempty subset of X, there is an element x in A such that $x \leq y$ for all y in A. In other words, every nonempty subset of X contains a "least element."

Note that this is a generalization of the structure of the positive (nonnegative) integers. The set of positive integers is well ordered by the usual < relation.

EXAMPLE 1.4.1

The set of all integers is not well ordered by the usual < relation. This set does have properties (i) and (ii) but not (iii). For the set of all negative integers is a nonempty subset of the set of integers but does not contain a least element.

EXAMPLE 1.4.2

The set of nonnegative real numbers is not well ordered by the usual < relation. Again, this set has properties (i) and (ii) but not (iii). For example, the set of all real numbers greater than 1, that is, $\{x : x$ is a real number and $x>1\}$, does not contain a least element; 1 is less than every element in the set but 1 is not in the set.

EXAMPLE 1.4.3

The set of all ordered pairs of nonnegative integers is well ordered by the lexicographic ordering <, in otherwords < is defined by $(n_1, n_2) < (n_3, n_4)$ if and only if $(n_1 < n_3)$ or $(n_1 = n_3$ and $n_2 < n_4)$. It is left as an exercise to show that this is indeed a well ordering.

We can now state a generalized induction principle for proving statements about any well ordered set.

THE GENERALIZED INDUCTION PRINCIPLE
    Let X be well ordered by <, and let $S(x)$ be a statement about an element x of X. If we wish to prove that $S(x)$ is true for all x in X we only need to:
    (i) Prove that $S(x_0)$ is true, where x_0 is the least element in X.
    (ii) Prove (for all $x_0<x$ in X) that if $S(y)$ is true for all $y<x$, then $S(x)$ is also true.
    Note that if X is the set of positive integers and < is the usual <, then the generalized induction principle

is identical to the strong induction principle of Section 1.3.

   To see that the generalized induction principle is a valid proof technique, suppose that $S(x)$ is some statement for which we have proven (i) and (ii). We want to conclude that $S(x)$ is true for all x in X. Suppose it is not. Then let $A = \{x : x$ is in X and $S(x)$ is false$\}$. If $S(x)$ is not true for all x in X, then A is a nonempty subset of X. Since X is well ordered, we know that A contains a least element a_0. By definition this is the least element of X for which $S(x)$ is false. Thus $S(y)$ is true for all y (if any) $< a_0$. If a_0 is the least element in X, then $S(a_0)$ is true by (i). Otherwise the fact that $S(y)$ is true for all $y < a_0$ together with (ii) implies that $S(a_0)$ is true. But this contradicts the fact that a_0 is in A and hence $S(a_0)$ is false. The only way to avoid this contradiction is if A is empty. In other words, there are no elements of X for which $S(x)$ is false.

EXAMPLE 1.4.4

Consider the sequence of numbers defined as follows:
$$s_{0,0} = 0$$

For any two nonnegative integers except 0,0, define
$$s_{m,n} = \begin{cases} s_{m-1,n}+1 & \text{if } n = 0 \\ s_{m,n-1}+1 & \text{otherwise, i.e., if } n \neq 0 \end{cases}$$

For example
$$s_{0,0} = 0 \quad s_{1,0} = s_{0,0}+1 = 0+1 = 1$$

$$s_{0,1} = s_{0,0}+1 = 1 \quad s_{1,1} = s_{1,0}+1 = 1+1 = 2$$

$$s_{2,0} = s_{1,0}+1 = 2 \quad s_{2,1} = s_{2,0}+1 = 3, \; \dots$$

Let us prove that for all nonnegative integers m,n that $s_{m,n} = m + n$. The proof will be by (generalized) induction on the set of ordered pairs of nonnegative integers, X, well ordered by the lexicographic ordering described in Example 1.4.3 (and Exercise 1 a). To prove that $s_{m,n} = m+n$ for all $\langle m,n \rangle$ in X, we only need to:

(i) Prove that $s_{m,n} = m+n$ is true where $\langle m,n \rangle$ is the least element in X. But since $\langle 0,0 \rangle$ is the least element in X, we need to show that $s_{0,0} = 0+0 = 0$. This is true by the definition of $s_{0,0}$.

(ii) Prove (for all $\langle 0,0 \rangle < \langle m,n \rangle$ in X) that if $s_{m',n'} = m' + n'$ is true for all $\langle m',n' \rangle < \langle m,n \rangle$, then $s_{m,n} = m+n$ is also true. To do so let us assume that $s_{m',n'} = m' + n'$ is true for all $\langle m',n' \rangle < \langle m,n \rangle$. This is the induction hypothesis. We then need to show that $s_{m,n} = m+n$. Either $n = 0$ or $n \neq 0$. If $n = 0$, then by definition $s_{m,n} = s_{m-1,n}+1$. But $\langle m-1,n \rangle < \langle m,n \rangle$, and, hence, by the induction hypothesis, $s_{m-1,n} = (m-1)+n$. Therefore, $s_{m,n} = s_{m-1,n}+1 = (m-1+n)+ 1=m+n$. If $n \neq 0$, then by definition $s_{m,n}= s_{m,n-1}+1$. But $\langle m,n-1 \rangle < \langle m,n \rangle$ and, thus, by the induction hypothesis, $s_{m,n-1} = m+(n-1)$. Therefore, for this case, $s_{m,n}= s_{m,n-1}+1=(m+n-1)+1=m+n$. This completes the proof.

EXERCISES

1. (a) Let $X = \{\langle n_1,n_2 \rangle : n_1$ and n_2 are nonnegative integers$\}$ and let $<$ be defined by $\langle n_1,n_2 \rangle < \langle n_3,n_4 \rangle$ if and only if $(n_1 < n_3)$ or $(n_1= n_3$ and $n_2<n_4)$ (where $<$ is the usual ordering on the integers).

Prove that $<$ well orders X. $<$ is called the lexico-graphic ordering.

(b) Prove the following more general result. Let $X = \{<x_1,x_2,\ldots,x_n> \mid x_1 \ \varepsilon \ X_1$ and $x_2 \ \varepsilon \ X_2 \ldots$ and $x_n \ \varepsilon \ X_n\}$. Suppose X_1 is well ordered by $<_1$ and X_2 is well ordered by $<_2$ and $\cdots X_n$ is well ordered by $<_n$. Then we can define the relation $<$ on X by

$$<x_1,x_2,\ldots,x_n> \ < \ <y_1,y_2,\ldots,y_n> \quad \text{if and only}$$
if $x_1 <_1 y_1$ or $(x_1 = y_1$ and $x_2 <_2 y_2)$ or $\ldots$ or
$(x_1 = y_1$ and $x_2 = y_2$ and $\ldots$ and $x_{n-1} = y_{n-1}$
and $x_n <_n y_n)$

Prove that $<$ well orders X.

2. Show that if X is well ordered by $<$, then there is no infinite sequence of elements $x_1, x_2, \ldots, x_n, \ldots$ in X such that $x_1 > x_2 > x_3 \cdots > x_n > \cdots$. In other words, no well-ordered set contains an infinite decreasing sequence of elements.

3. Suppose $S(n_1, n_2, \cdots, n_m)$ is a statement about m nonnegative integers $n_1, n_2, \cdots, n_m$. Using the generalized induction principle and lexicographic ordering, state what must be proved in order to prove the $S(n_1, n_2, \cdots, n_m)$ is true for all non-negative integers $n_1, n_2, \cdots, n_m$.

4. Consider the sequence of numbers defined as follows:

$$S_{1,1} = 5$$

For all pairs of positive integers m,n, except 1,1, define

$$s_{m,n} = \begin{cases} s_{m-1,n}+2 & \text{if } n=1 \\ s_{m,n-1}+2 & \text{if } n\neq 1 \end{cases}$$

Prove by (generalized) induction that for all pairs of positive integers m,n,

$$s_{m,n} = 2\cdot(m+n)+1$$

5. Consider the sequence of numbers defined as follows:

$$s_{0,0} = 0$$

For all pairs of nonnegative integers $\underline{m}, \underline{n}$, except 0,0, define

$$s_{m,n} = \begin{cases} s_{m-1,n}+1 & \text{if } n=0 \\ s_{m,n-1}+n & \text{if } n\neq 0 \end{cases}$$

Prove by (generalized) induction that for all pairs of nonnegative integers $m,\ n$,

$$s_{m,n} = \frac{n(n+1)}{2} + m$$

6. Consider the sequence of numbers defined as follows:

$$s_{0,0} = 1$$

For all pairs of nonnegative integers m,n, except 0,0, define

$$s_{m,n} = \begin{cases} s_{m-1,n} + m & \text{if } n=0 \\ s_{m,n-1} + n & \text{if } n\neq 0 \end{cases}$$

Figure out a formula for $s_{m,n}$ and prove it by (generalized) induction.

7. (a) Let X be the set of all integers n such that $n_0 \leq n \leq m_0$.   Let $<_1$ be the usual $<$ ordering for

integers restricted to this set.   Note that x is well ordered by $<_1$ and that generalized induction on X, well ordered by $<_1$, is the same as strong, upward induction mentioned in Exercise 8 of Section 1.3. (b)   Let X be the same set as in part (a) but let $<_2$ be defined by $n_1 <_2 n_2$ if and only if $n_2 < n_1$ where $<$ is the usual ordering on the integers. Show that X is well ordered by $<_2$.   Would the same ordering $<_2$ defined on the set of all nonnegative integers be a well-ordering?   Show that generalized induction on the set X, well ordered by $<_2$, is the same as strong, downward induction mentioned in Exercise 8 of Section 1.3.

CHAPTER TWO

PROVING THE CORRECTNESS OF FLOWCHART PROGRAMS

2.1   INTRODUCTION

When we write a computer program, our intention is that it carry out some particular computation. However, as all programmers are painfully aware, most of our programs have errors (or bugs) in them. Thus we normally spend a large percentage of our programming time testing and debugging the (incorrect) programs we have written. Even when we have finished testing and debugging a program, we cannot be certain that it is completely correct. All we can be sure of is that he program gives the correct results for the particular data we used to test it. Later, when the program is used with different data, still another bug may appear. Every experienced programmer knows of programs that had run correctly over a long period of time and thus appeared almost certainly to be correct, when suddenly another bug mysteriously appeared in the program. Hence testing, no matter how extensive, can never really assure us that a program is correct.

Ideally, we should prove that the program is correct rather than depending solely on testing it. Of course, even if we manage to give a proof that the program is correct, we cannot be absolutely certain that it is. For proofs can have errors (bugs) in them just as programs do. Nonetheless, the process of attempting to prove that a program is correct is very helpful in forcing one to thoroughly comprehend the program. One can only prove a program correct by understanding it very thoroughly. Experience has shown that for this reason, correctness proofs are helpful in uncovering bugs one might otherwise overlook.

If we could formalize correctness proofs and have them checked by an absolutely reliable source (an automatic proof checker), then we could have complete confidence in them. This may be possible in the future (see Chapter 5) but is impractical at the present time. We will be dealing with informally expressed correctness proofs. Experience with such informal proofs indicates that they do increase ones confidence in and understanding of programs and are thus worthwhile, even though they do not bring absolute certainty. Such informal crrectness proofs can be viewed as a very systematic form of desk checking a program -- something all good programmers do anyway. This chapter introduces the basic ideas of such correctness proofs for flowchart programs.

2.2   BASIC PRINCIPLES OF PROVING FLOWCHART PROGRAMS CORRECT

If we wish to prove that some program is correct, of course we must be able to write down a description of what the program is supposed to accomplish. Let us refer to such a description as the correctness statement or assertion. A proof that the program is correct then consists of a proof that the program, when executed, will eventually terminate (stop) and, when it does terminate, the correctness assertion will be true. Often a program is only required to work correctly for certain values of the input data. If this is the case, the correctness proof would consist of a proof that, whenever the program is executed with appropriate input data, it will eventually terminate and, when it does terminate, the correctness assertion will be true.

Let us illustrate these ideas with the correctness proof for a very simple flowchart program.

EXAMPLE   2.2.1

Suppose we wish to compute the product of any two integers M,N such that $M \geq 0$ without using the operation of multiplication. One way to do this is to add N to itself M times. The result will be $M \cdot N$. Consider the following flowchart program, which implements this computation.

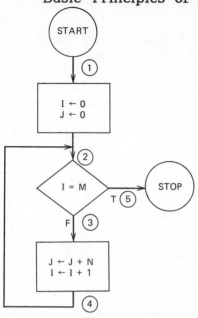

We wish to prove that this program correctly computes the product of any two integers M and N provided that M ≥ 0; that is, whenever the program is executed with M and N already having integer values and M ≥ 0, it will eventually terminate (reach point 5) with J = M·N.

In order to check that the flowchart works correctly, we could test it with some specific data. for example, let us do a hand simulation of the execution of the program with the data M = 3 and N = 5.

The following table shows the values of the variables I and J each time execution reaches point 2 (the loop point) in the flowchart.

For M = 3, N = 5

The Number of Times, n, That Execution Has Reached Point 2	Value of I	Value of J
1	0	0
2	1	5
3	2	10
4	3	15

The fourth time execution reaches point 2, the value of I is 3, which is equal to M, and therefore execution will leave the loop and proceed to point 5.

When execution reaches point 5 , J = 15 = 3·5 = M·N. Thus we see that the flowchart works correctly for the specific data, M = 3, N = 5. Even though this tends to convince us that the program works correctly, it certainly does not prove that the program works correctly for all possible values of M and N. We can now continue to test the program with different data for M and N. If it ever computes a wrong answer, we would of course know that it is incorrect. However, if it continues to compute correct answers, we may gain confidence in the program, but we will never be certain that it computes correct answers for all possible values of M and N (there will always be an infinite number of possible values for which the program has not been tested). Of course, on any real computer, the values of M and N are restricted to some finite range of integer numbers. Thus in principle the program could be exhaustively tested on this range of numbers. However for most computers this range is so large as to make exhaustive testing completely inpractical. Furthermore, we normally design such programs to work correctly, regardless of the size of M and N. Hence we should only be satisfied if we can demonstrate that the program works correctly regardless of the size of M and N. This we can never accomplish by testing.

The Number of Times, n, That Execution Has Reached Point 2	Value of I	Value of J
1	0	0
2	1	N
3	2	2·N
4	3	3·N
.	.	.
.	.	.
.	.	.
M+1	M	M·N

Suppose that instead of executing the program with specific data for M and N, we execute it with the symbolic data M, N. Then we would obtain the previous trace of the values of I, J each time execution reaches point 2.

Thus we see that when execution has proceeded around the loop M times (so that execution has reached point 2 for the M+1th time), the value of I is M and the value of J is M·N. At this point I's value is equal to M, and hence execution will leave the loop and proceed to point 5. Thus, when execution reaches point 5 and terminates, we will have J = M·N. This shows that the program works correctly for any values of M and N. Nevertheless, notice that the trace assumes that M ≥ 0 so that I's value (which starts at 0 and increases by 1 each time around the loop) will eventually equal M. If M < 0, then execution would proceed around the loop forever without I's value ever being equal to M, and hence execution would fail to terminate. Thus the flowchart really works correctly only for M ≥ 0. For any integer values of M, N such that M ≥ 0, the above trace shows that the flowchart eventually terminates with J = M·N.

However, notice that there is a gap in the table represented by three dots. How did we figure out what I and J's values were after the gap in the table? And how can we be sure that they are as shown? The answer to the first question is that by tracing the flowchart and filling in the first part of the table, we came to understand how I and J's values change each time around the loop (we saw a pattern to these changes) and used this understanding (inductively) to figure out what the values of I and J would be the M+1th time execution reaches point 2. The answer to the second question is that to be really sure we should prove it.

We can see from the table that each time execution reaches point 2, we have J = I·N. Let us prove this by induction on the number of times n that execution has reached point 2 (see the last paragraph of Section 1.2 for a thorough explanation of such inductive proofs).

(i)   The first time (n=1) execution reaches point 2 (coming from point 1), we have I = 0 and J = 0 and thus J = I·N = 0·N = 0 is true.

(ii) Suppose that $J = I \cdot N$ is true the nth time execution reaches point 2. We need to show that if execution returns to point 2 for an n+1th time, then $J = I \cdot N$ will again be true. Let us denote the values of I and J the nth time execution reaches point 2 by I_n, J_n. Thus the induction hypothesis would be that $J_n = I_n \cdot N$. The only way that execution can return to point 2 for an n+1th time is to proceed around the loop (to points 3, 4 and back to point 2). If it does so, then we can see by tracing execution around the loop once that when execution returns to point 2, I's new value is its old value +1 and J's new value is its old value +N. That is,

$$I_{n+1} = I_n + 1 \text{ and } J_{n+1} = J_n + N$$

$$J_{n+1} = I_n \cdot N + N \text{ by the induction hypothesis}$$

$$= (I_n + 1) \cdot N$$

$$= I_{n+1} \cdot N$$

Thus we see that if execution returns to point 2 for a n+1th time, again, $J = I \cdot N$. This completes the induction proof and shows that each time execution reaches point 2, the statement $J = I \cdot N$ is true.

The only way for execution to terminate (stop going around the loop) is to reach point 2 with the test $I = M$ true. At that point execution would be at point 2 with $I = M$ and $J = I \cdot N = M \cdot N$. Execution would then proceed to point 5 and terminate with $J = M \cdot N$. However, please note that we have not yet shown that execution does in fact terminate. All we have shown is that each time execution reaches point 2, $J = I \cdot N$ and, thus, if execution does ever terminate, $J = M \cdot N$. To see this more clearly, note that the proof that $J = I \cdot N$ each time execution reaches point 2 did not depend on whether $M \geq 0$ or not. Hence, even if $M < 0$, that proof would still be correct and would show that each time execution reaches point 2, $J = I \cdot N$. However, if $M < 0$, execution will proceed around the loop forever without I's value ever being equal to M and thus execution will not

terminate and will not correctly compute J = M·N.   It
will be true, however, even in this case (M < 0), that
each time execution reaches point 2, J = I·N (this must
be the case or the previous proof was incorrect). Check
this carefully for yourself by tracing execution of the
flowchart with M having some value < 0.   You will see
that for such an M, execution never terminates, but it is
still true that each time execution reaches point 2, J=I·N.

   Thus we still need to prove that the flowchart
terminates.   To do this we need the assumption about
the data, namely that M ≧ 0.   We want to prove that if
M ≧ 0, then eventually execution will reach point 2 with
I = M.   This is quite apparent from the flowchart, since
I's value is initialized to 0 and is increased by 1 each
time around the loop.   Thus it must eventually increase
to be equal to M, provided that M is an integer and
M ≧ 0.   However, if we want to be very rigorous about
this, we can also prove this fact by induction.

   If M ≧ 0, let us prove by upward induction on m
that for each value of m, such that 0 ≦ m ≦ M, execution
eventually reaches point 2 with I = m.

(i)   The first time execution reaches point 2 we
      have I = 0.   Thus the statement is true for
      m = 0.   If M = 0, then this proves the result.

(ii) Otherwise suppose that execution does eventual-
      ly reach point 2 with I = m and 0 ≦ m < M.
      We need to show that execution will also reach
      point 2 with I = m + 1.   When execution is at
      point 2 with I = m and 0 ≦ m < M, we will
      have that the test I = M is false, since m < M
      and hence execution will proceed around the
      loop and return to point 2.   When it returns
      to point 2, I's value will have been increased
      by 1, and hence we see that execution will
      eventually reach point 2 with I = m+1.   This
      completes the proof by upward induction.

   From the proceeding, we may conclude that if M ≧ 0,
then execution will eventually reach point 2 with I = M.
At that point, the test I = M will be true and execution
will proceed to point 5 and terminate.

   We have now proven in (excessive) detail that if
this flowchart is executed with M and N being any two
integer numbers and M ≧ 0, then execution will eventually terminate and when it does, we will have J = M·N.

EXAMPLE 2.2.2

We have given the preceeding proof in more detail than is really necessary. Let us now repeat this proof leaving out some of the detail and formality of the induction proofs. In particular, in proving that a statement is true each time execution reaches some point inside a simple loop like the one in the previous flowchart, all we need to show is that (i) the statement is true the first time execution reaches that point, and (ii) if execution is at the point and the statement is true (the induction hypothesis), and execution proceeds around the loop and returns to the point, then the statement will again be true. If we can prove (i) and (ii) then, by filling in the details, we can prove (by induction on the number of times that execution has reached the point) that each time execution reaches the point the statement is true. In giving the second version of this correctness proof, we also attach the key assertions that we wish to prove directly to the points in the flowchart to which they refer. This helps us to keep clearly in mind the key steps of the correctness proof.

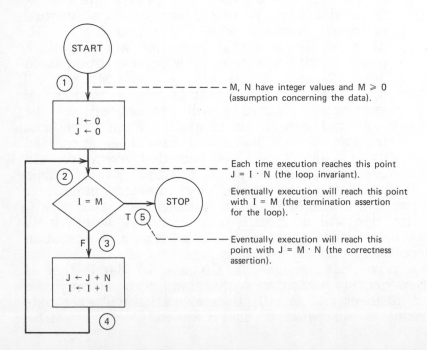

M, N have integer values and M ⩾ 0 (assumption concerning the data).

Each time execution reaches this point J = I · N (the loop invariant).

Eventually execution will reach this point with I = M (the termination assertion for the loop).

Eventually execution will reach this point with J = M · N (the correctness assertion).

Now let us prove that the above flowchart is correct, that is, if it is executed with M, N having integer values with $M \geq 0$, then eventually execution will terminate with $J = M \cdot N$.

First let us prove that each time execution reaches point 2, $J = I \cdot N$.

(i)   The first time execution reaches point 2 (by proceeding from point 1 to point 2), $I = 0$ and $J = 0$. Thus it will be true that $J = I \cdot N = 0 \cdot N = 0$.

(ii)   Suppose execution is at point 2 and $J = I \cdot N$ is true. Let us call I and J's values at this point I_n and J_n so that we have $J_n = I_n \cdot N$. Now suppose execution proceeds around the loop (from point 2 to 3, 4 and back to 2). When execution returns to point 2, the new values of I and J, which we denote as I_{n+1} and J_{n+1}, will be

$$I_{n+1} = I_n + 1$$

$$J_{n+1} = I_n \cdot N + N \text{ (since } J_n = I_n \cdot N)$$

$$= (I_n + 1) \cdot N$$

$$= I_{n+1} \cdot N$$

Thus, upon returning to point 2, we again have that $J = I \cdot N$ is true. This completes the proof that each time execution reaches point 2, $J = I \cdot N$.

Next let us prove that eventually execution will reach point 2 with $I = M$. The first time execution reaches point 2, $I = 0$. Each succeeding time (if any) that execution reaches point 2, I's value is increased by 1. Since M's value is never changed by the flowchart and since we are assuming that $M \geq 0$, it is apparent that I's value will eventually increase to equal M.

When execution reaches point 2 with $I = M$, we will also have $J = I \cdot N = M \cdot N$. At that point the test $I = M$ will be true, and execution will follow the true arrow to point 5. Thus execution will eventually reach point 5 with $J = M \cdot N$. This completes the correctness proof.

EXAMPLE 2.2.3

The next program we wish to prove correct is one for computing the integer quotient, IQ, and remainder, IR, of J1 divided by J2, where J1 and J2 are any two integers with $0 \leq J1$ and $1 \leq J2$. The flowchart computes IQ and IR without using division. One way to express what the flowchart is supposed to compute is to say that it computes two integer numbers IQ, IR so that $J1/J2 = IQ + IR/J2$ and $0 \leq IR < J2$. Rewriting this, $J1 = IQ \cdot J2 + IR$ and $0 \leq IR < J2$. As in the previous example, we attach directly to the flowchart any assumptions about the data and the facts that we wish to prove about the flowchart.

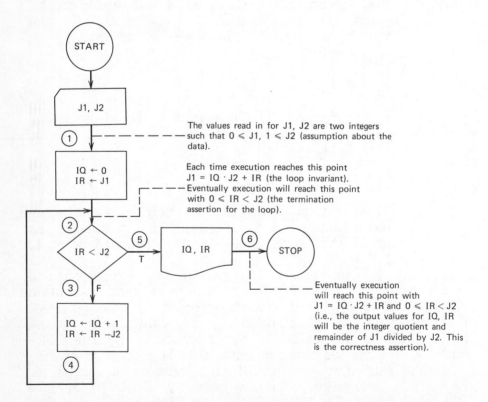

The values read in for J1, J2 are two integers such that $0 \leq J1$, $1 \leq J2$ (assumption about the data).

Each time execution reaches this point $J1 = IQ \cdot J2 + IR$ (the loop invariant). Eventually execution will reach this point with $0 \leq IR < J2$ (the termination assertion for the loop).

Eventually execution will reach this point with $J1 = IQ \cdot J2 + IR$ and $0 \leq IR < J2$ (i.e., the output values for IQ, IR will be the integer quotient and remainder of J1 divided by J2. This is the correctness assertion).

Note that we have attached the assumption about the values that are read in for J1 and J2 to the point in the flowchart immediately below the input box. This is to indicate that we are only trying to prove that the program works correctly for input data that satisfy these assumptions. We have attached the assertion that expresses the correctness of the flowchart to the terminal point of the flowchart. In addition, we have attached two key facts that we need to prove about the loop to the beginning point of the loop. Now let us do a trace of the flowchart execution with symbolic data for J1 and J2 and see how we arrived at the key loop assertion (the loop invariant)

The Number of Times, n, Execution Has Reached Point 2	IQ	IR
1	0	J1
2	1	J1 - J2
3	2	J1 - 2·J2
4	3	J1 - 3·J2
.	.	.
.	.	Until.IR<J2
.	.	.

Note that each time execution reaches point 2, we have
$$IR = J1 - IQ \cdot J2$$
or, rewriting this,
$$J1 = IQ \cdot J2 + IR$$
This is identical to the correctness assertion execpt that it is also necessary that $0 \leq IR < J2$. Thus, we also need to show that the loop eventually terminates and when it does, $0 \leq IR < J2$. The student can see that the statements attached to point 2 in the flowchart essentially express these facts about the loop.

In order to prove the flowchart is correct, let us first prove that each time execution reaches point 2 in the flowchart, $J1 = IQ \cdot J2 + IR$.

    (i)   The first time execution reaches point 2 (by proceeding from START to 2), we have IQ = 0 and IR = J1.
            Thus the assertion:

$$J1 = IQ \cdot J2 + IR$$

$$= 0 \cdot J2 + J1$$

$$= 0 + J1$$

$$= J1$$

will be true.

(ii) Suppose execution is at point 2 and $J1 = IQ \cdot J2 + IR$ is true. Let us call IQ and IR's values at this point IQ_n and IR_n. We assume the assertion is true at this point, that is, $J1 = IQ_n \cdot J2 + IR_n$ (the induction hypothesis). Now suppose that execution proceeds around the loop (from point 2 to 3, 4 and back to 2). When execution returns to point 2, IQ and IR's new values are $IQ_{n+1} = IQ_n + 1$ and $IR_{n+1} = IR_n - J2$. Thus we will have

$$IQ_{n+1} \cdot J2 + IR_{n+1} = (IQ_n + 1) \cdot J2 + (IR_n - J2)$$

$$= IQ_n \cdot J2 + J2 + IR_n - J2$$

$$= IQ_n \cdot J2 + IR_n$$

$$= J1 \qquad \text{(by the induction hypothesis)}$$

This completes the proof that each time execution reaches point 2, $J1 = IQ \cdot J2 + IR$.

Next let us prove that eventually execution will reach point 2 with $0 \le IR < J2$. To do this, let us first prove that each time execution reaches point 2, $0 \le IR$.

(i) The first time execution reaches point 2 we have $IR = J1$ and, by assumption, $0 \le J1$. (Note that this is the only place where this assumption is used in the proof. Thus, if we didn't require that IR $\geq$ 0, the flowchart would work correctly, even for negative values of J1).

(ii) Suppose execution is at point 2 and $0 \leq$ IR. Let us call its value at this point IR_n. If execution proceeds from point 2 around the loop, when execution returns to point 2, IR's new value is $IR_{n+1} = IR_n$ - J2. But execution will proceed around the loop only if the test $IR_n <$ J2 is false, that is, only if $J2 \leq IR_n$. But if $J2 \leq IR_n$, then $0 \leq IR_n$ -J2 = IR_{n+1} is true. This completes the proof that each time execution reaches point 2 $0 \leq$ IR.

Next let us prove that eventually execution reaches point 2 with IR < J2 (so that, at that point, we would have $0 \leq$ IR < J2). Note that each time around the loop, IR's value is decreased by subtracting J2's value from it. Since J2's value is never changed by the flowchart and since, by assumption, $1 \leq$ J2, we see that this decreases IR's value by at least 1 each time around the loop. Hence IR's value must eventually decrease to be less than J2 (as usual, this informal proof could be made rigorous by induction -- see Exercise 7).

Thus eventually execution will reach point 2 with $0 \leq$ IR < J2 and J1 = IQ $\cdot$ J2 + IR. At that point the test IR < J2 will be true and execution will pass from point 2 to point 5 and then to 6. Since none of the variables have their values changed between point 2 and point 6, it is obvious that the correctness assertion will be true when execution reaches point 6. Thus we have proven that any time this flowchart is executed with the values read in for J1 and J2 being two integers such that $0 \leq$ J1 and $1 \leq$ J2, execution will eventually terminate with J1 = IQ $\cdot$ J2 + IR and $0 \leq$ IR < J2; that is, with IQ and IR being the integer quotient and remainder of J1 divided by J2.

EXERCISES

1. Prove that flowchart a) computes the product of M and N, provided that M and N already have integer values and M ≥ 0. What happens if M < 0?

2. Suppose the test in flowchart a) had mistakenly been I = 1 rather than I = 0. Which steps(s) of the correctness proof would fail? Suppose J had mistakenly been initialized to 1 rather than 0. Which step(s) of the correctness proof would fail? Suppose J was initialized to N rather than 0 and the flowchart test was changed to I = 1. For what values of the data would the flowchart correctly compute M · N? How would this show up in the correctness proof?

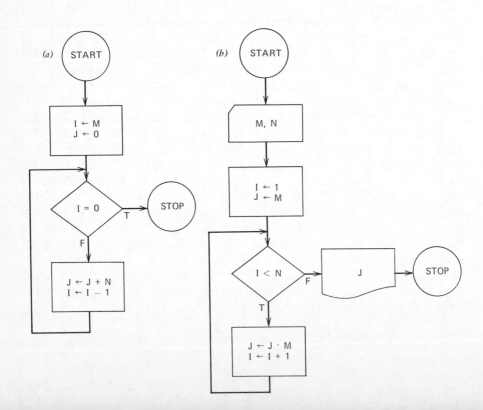

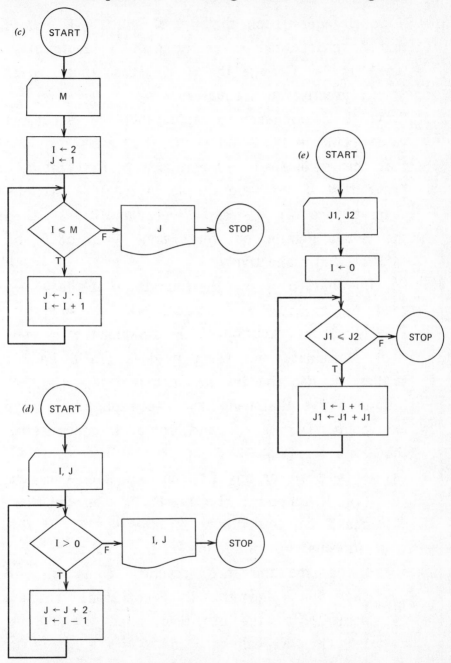

3. Prove that flowchart b) computes and prints out the
    value of M^N provided the values read in for M and

N are integers such that $1 \leq M$ and $1 \leq N$. Does this flowchart work correctly if the value inputted for N is 0? Change the flowchart so that it does work correctly for N equal 0.

4. Prove that flowchart c) computes and prints out the value of $M! = 1 \cdot 2 \cdot 3 \cdots (M - 1) \cdot M$, provided that the value read in for M is a positive integer.

5. Prove that if the values read in for I, J in flowchart d) are I_0, J_0, respectively, and $0 \leq I_0$, then the values printed out for I and J will be 0 and $J_0 + 2 \cdot I_0$, respectively.

6. For flowchart e) prove the following. If the values read in for J1, J2 are integers $J1_0$, $J2_0$ such that $1 \leq J1_0$, then execution of the flowchart will eventually terminate and when it does I will be the smallest nonnegative integer such that $J2_0 < J1_0 \cdot 2^I$. Hint -- Prove that each time execution reaches the loop point, $J1 = J1_0 \cdot 2^I$ and, for all integers i such that $0 \leq i < I$, $J1_0 \cdot 2^i \leq J2_0$.

7. (a) Show that for any flowchart of the basic form (i), if for all I, $I + 1 \leq F(I)$, then the flowchart loop eventually terminates. Prove this rigorously by induction on the number of times that execution has reached point 2. In particular, show that if execution has reached point 2 for the nth time, then $I \geq I_0 + n - 1$. Thus we will know for $n_0 = M - I_0 + 2$ (or $n_0 = 1$ if $M < I_0$) that after execution reaches point 2, at most n_0 times, $I \geq I_0 + (M - I_0$

+ 2) - 1 = M + 1.   And   hence,   eventually
(after at most n_0 times), execution will reach
point 2 with the test $I \leq M$ being false and
will exit from the loop.

(b) Show that for any flowchart of the basic form
(ii), if for all I, $G(I) \leq I - 1$, then the flowchart eventually terminates. Prove this rigorously by induction.

In most of the correctness proofs we will give
rather informal proofs of the termination of loops. This
problem is designed to show that these could be made
more rigorous.

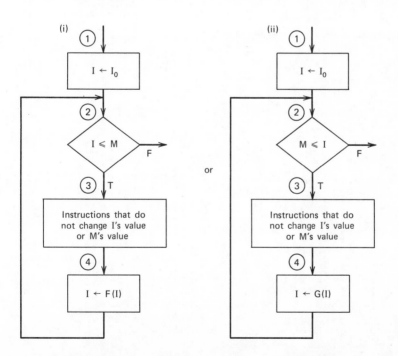

8.   For each of the following flowcharts determine for
what values of the data the flowchart terminates.

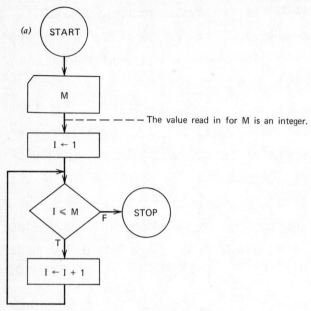

(a)

M

The value read in for M is an integer.

$I \leftarrow 1$

$I \leqslant M$ — F → STOP

T

$I \leftarrow I + 1$

(b) Same as (a) except the test $I < M$ is replaced by the test $I = M$.

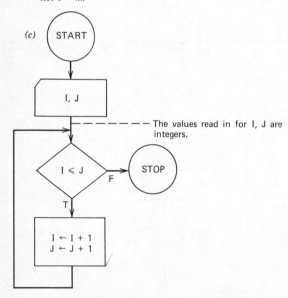

(c)

I, J

The values read in for I, J are integers.

$I \leqslant J$ — F → STOP

T

$I \leftarrow I + 1$
$J \leftarrow J + 1$

(d) Same as (c), except the instruction $I \leftarrow I + 1$
is replaced by $I \leftarrow I + 2$.

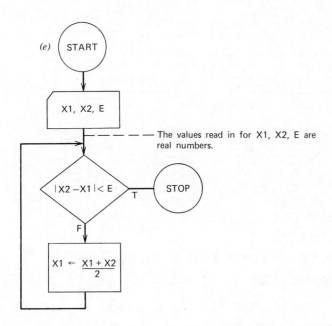

(e)

START

X1, X2, E

— — — — — The values read in for X1, X2, E are real numbers.

$|X2 - X1| < E$ T   STOP

F

$X1 \leftarrow \dfrac{X1 + X2}{2}$

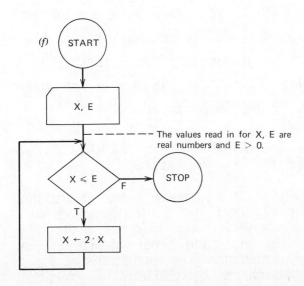

(f)

START

X, E

— — — — — The values read in for X, E are real numbers and $E > 0$.

$X \leq E$ F   STOP

T

$X \leftarrow 2 \cdot X$

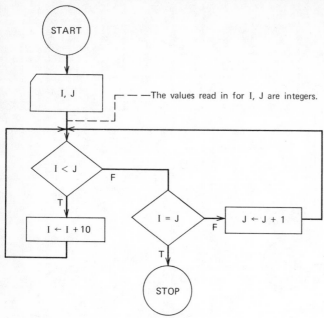

(h) Same as (g), except that the instruction J ← J + 1 is replaced by J ← J + 2.

9. For flowcharts 8(e) and (f), give formal induction proofs of termination. For example, 8(f) terminates for any value of X>0. Prove this by induction on the number of times n that execution has reached the loop point. In particular, show that if the value read in for X is $X_0 > 0$, then the nth time execution reaches the loop point, $X = 2^{n-1} \cdot X_0$.

2.3 ADDITIONAL EXAMPLES OF CORRECTNESS PROOFS FOR FLOWCHARTS

In this section we will present some additional examples of correctness proofs for flowchart programs. The proofs will be presented in an informal style with some of the detail of the induction proofs deleted. You should discover for yourself the key assertions attached to the loops in the flowcharts by tracing the execution of the flowchart with symbolic data and keeping track of what is true each time execution reaches the loop point.

EXAMPLE 2.3.1

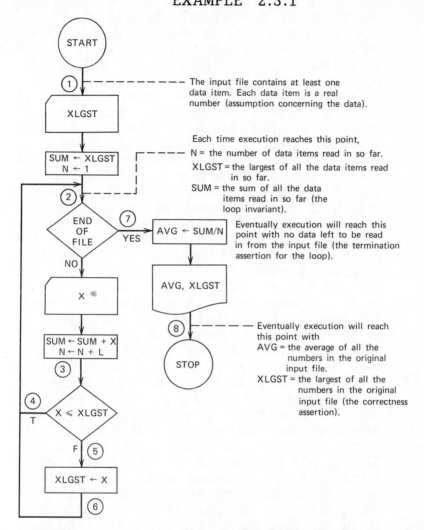

The input file contains at least one data item. Each data item is a real number (assumption concerning the data).

Each time execution reaches this point,

N = the number of data items read in so far.

XLGST = the largest of all the data items read in so far.

SUM = the sum of all the data items read in so far (the loop invariant).

Eventually execution will reach this point with no data left to be read in from the input file (the termination assertion for the loop).

Eventually execution will reach this point with

AVG = the average of all the numbers in the original input file.

XLGST = the largest of all the numbers in the original input file (the correctness assertion).

We wish to prove that the above flowchart computes and prints out the average and largest of all the numbers in the input file. Let us first prove that the assertion attached to point 2 is true.

    (i)   If the above flowchart is executed with an input file consisting of one or more real numbers, then the first input box can be executed (since the input file will not be empty) and, when execution reaches point 2 for the first time, the value of N will be 1 and the values of both XLGST and SUM will be the first number in the original input file. Thus the first time execution reaches point 2, the assertions about N, XLGST, and SUM will be true.

(ii) Suppose execution is at point 2 and the assertions about N, XLGST, and SUM are true. We need to show that if execution proceeds around the loop and returns to point 2 then the assertions will again be true. Note that each time around the loop one more value is read in for X from the input file (which is definitely not empty or execution would not proceed around the loop), and N's value is increased by 1 and SUM's value is set to SUM + X. Therefore, when execution returns to point 2, N's value will again be the number of data items read in so far (namely 1 more than before), and SUM's value will again be the sum of all the data items read in so far (namely the sum of all the previous data items plus the one additional data item that was read in). Also note that each time around the loop XLGST, which is assumed to be the largest of all the previous data items read in, is compared to the one additional data item that was read in for X. If $X \leq XLGST$ is true, then the flowchart does not change XLGST and this is correct, since its present value is still the largest of all the data items read in so far. However, if $X \leq XLGST$ is false, then the last item read in is the largest of all the data items read in so far, and note that in this case the flowchart correctly sets XLGST to X. Thus when execution returns to point 2 (whether by the path from point 2, to 3, to 4, and back to 2, or the path from point 2, to 3, to 5, to 6, and back to 2), XLGST will again be the largest of all the data items read in so far. This completes the proof that each time execution reaches point 2 the assertions about N, XLGST, and SUM are true.

It is clear that execution will eventually reach point 2 with no data left to be read in from the input file, since each time around the loop one more data item is read in and we (implicitly) assume that the input file contains only a finite number of items. Hence, after some finite number of times around the loop, all the data items will have been inputted. Of course when this happens the test for the end of file will give the answer YES, and execution will leave the loop with N, XLGST, and SUM having the values:

N = the number of data items read in so far.

= the total number of data items in the original input file (since all items in the input file have been read in).

XLGST = the largest of all the data items in the original input file.

SUM = the sum of all the data items in the original input file.

Execution will then proceed to point 8, and when it reaches point 8, AVG will have the value AVG = SUM/N and XLGST will still have the value stated above. Thus the flowchart will eventually terminate, and when it does, AVG and XLGST will have the correct values.

EXAMPLE 2.3.2

Presented on the next page is the Euclidean algorithm for finding the greatest common divisor of any two positive integers.

GCD (X,Y) stands for the greatest common divisior of X and Y, that is, the largest integer that divides both integer X and integer Y without remainder. REMAINDER (X, Y) stands for the integer remainder of integer X divided by integer Y. The Euclidean algorithm is based on the following mathematical result. For any two positive integers $0 \leq X \leq Y$, GCD (X, Y) = GCD [REMAINDER (Y, X), X]. We use this fact in our correctness proof for this flowchart.

Let us first prove that each time execution reaches point 2, $0 \leq S \leq L$ and GCD (S, L) = GCD (A, B).

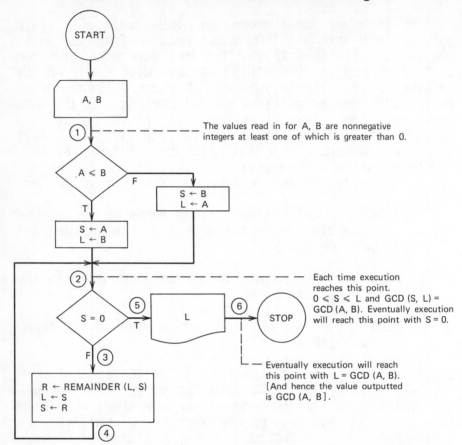

The values read in for A, B are nonnegative integers at least one of which is greater than 0.

Each time execution reaches this point. $0 \leqslant S \leqslant L$ and GCD (S, L) = GCD (A, B). Eventually execution will reach this point with S = 0.

Eventually execution will reach this point with L = GCD (A, B). [And hence the value outputted is GCD (A, B].

(i)   The first time execution reaches point 2 (from point 1), either S = A and L = B and $A \leq B$ is true or S = B and L = A and $A \leq B$ is false. In either case, $S \leq L$ and GCD (S, L) = GCD (A, B). The assumptions about the data are that both A and B are nonnegative integers and hence the first time execution reaches point 2, regardless of whether S = A or S = B, it will be true that $0 \leq S$. Therefore, the first time execution reaches point 2, we will have $0 \leq S \leq L$ and GCD (S, L) = GCD (A, B).

(ii) Suppose execution is at point 2 and the assertion $0 \leq S \leq L$ and GCD (S, L) = GCD (A, B) is true. Let us call the values of S and L at that point S_n and L_n so that we have $0 \leq S_n \leq L_n$ and GCD (S_n, L_n) = GCD (A, B) (the induction hypothesis). If execution proceeds around the loop and returns to point 2, S and L's new values would be S_{n+1}=R=REMAINDER (L_n, S_n) and $L_{n+1} = S_n$. Using the fundamental mathematical result stated earlier, we would then have GCD (S_{n+1}, L_n+1)

$= $ GCD [REMAINDER (L_n, S_n), $S_n]$

$= $ GCD (S_n, L_n) (by the mathematical result)

$= $ GCD (A, B) (by the induction hypothesis)

Also, we know that $0 \leq$ REMAINDER (L_n, S_n) $< S_n$ and hence $0 \leq S =$ REMAINDER (L_n, S_n) $\leq L_{n+1} = S_n$. This completes the proof that each time execution reaches point 2, $0 \leq S \leq L$ and GCD $(S, L) = $ GCD (A, B).

Let us next prove that execution eventually reaches point 2 with S = 0. Each time execution proceeds around the loop, S is set to REMAINDER (L, S). But we know that REMAINDER (L, S) < S and thus we see that S's value is decreased by at least 1 each time around the loop. We also know that $0 \leq S$ each time execution reaches point 2. Thus S must eventually decrease to be equal to 0.

At that point, execution would be at 2 with S=0 and GCD(S, L) = GCD(0, L) = GCD(A, B). But the GCD(0, L) = L, since clearly L divides both 0 and L without remainder and is the largest integer that does so. Thus at that point the test S = 0 would be true, and execution would proceed to point 6 with L=GCD(0,L) = GCD(A, B).

EXAMPLE 2.3.3

We wish to prove that the following flowchart correctly computes the SUM, $\sum_{J=1}^{N} X_J = X_1 + X_2 + \cdots + X_N$. Let us first prove that each time execution reaches point 2, $1 \leq I \leq N + 1$ and SUM $= \sum_{J=1}^{I-1} X_J = X_1 + \cdots + X_{I-1}$.

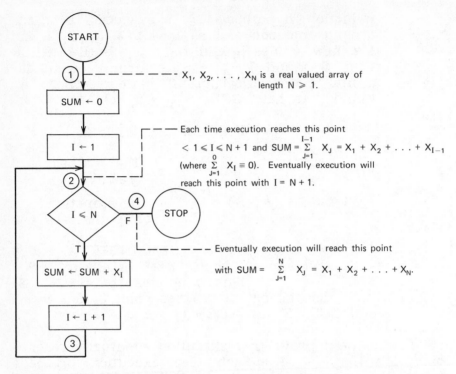

(i)   The first time execution reaches point 2 $I = 1$ and $SUM = 0$, and thus the assertion that $1 \leq I \leq N + 1$ and $SUM = \sum_{J=1}^{I-1} X_J = \sum_{J=1}^{0} X_J \equiv 0$ is true.

(ii) Suppose execution is at point 2 and $1 \leq I \leq N + 1$ and $SUM = \sum_{J=1}^{I-1} X_J$ is true. Let us call the values of I and SUM at this point I_n and SUM_n so that we have $1 \leq I_n \leq N+1$ and $SUM_n = \sum_{n}^{I_n-1} X_J = X_1 + X_2 + \cdots X_{I_n-1}$. If execution proceeds around the loop, when it returns to point 2, we will have

$$I_{n+1} = I_n + 1$$

and

$$SUM_{n+1} = SUM_n + X_{I_n}$$

$$= (X_1 + X_2 + \cdots X_{I_{n-1}}) + X_{I_n}$$

$$= \sum_{J=1}^{I_n} X_J$$

$$= \sum_{J=1}^{(I_n+1)-1} X_J$$

$$= \sum_{J=1}^{I_{n+1}-1} X_J$$

Also, if execution proceeds around the loop, we know that the test $I_n \leq N$ is true as well as $1 \leq I_n \leq N+1$ and hence $1 \leq I_n \leq N$. But then, when execution returns to point 2, $1 < 2 \leq I_n + 1 = I_{n+1} \leq N+1$. This completes the proof that each time execution reaches point 2, $1 \leq I \leq N+1$ and $SUM = \sum_{J=1}^{I-1} X_J$.

It is easy to see that if $1 \leq N$, I's value will eventually increase from 1 to be equal to $N+1$. At that point, the test $I \leq N$ will be false and execution will proceed to point 4. When it does, we will have $SUM = \sum_{J=1}^{I-1} X_J$ and $I = N+1$. Thus we will have $SUM = \sum_{J=1}^{(N+1)-1} X_J = \sum_{J=1}^{N} X_J$. This completes the proof that execution will eventually terminate (reach point 4) with $SUM = \sum_{J=1}^{N} X_J$.

EXAMPLE 2.3.4

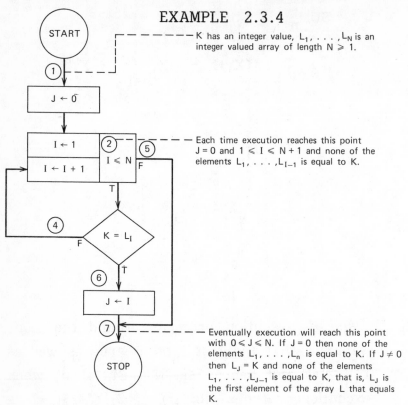

K has an integer value, $L_1, \ldots, L_N$ is an integer valued array of length $N \geqslant 1$.

Each time execution reaches this point $J = 0$ and $1 \leqslant I \leqslant N + 1$ and none of the elements $L_1, \ldots, L_{I-1}$ is equal to K.

Eventually execution will reach this point with $0 \leqslant J \leqslant N$. If $J = 0$ then none of the elements $L_1, \ldots, L_n$ is equal to K. If $J \neq 0$ then $L_J = K$ and none of the elements $L_1, \ldots, L_{J-1}$ is equal to K, that is, L_J is the first element of the array L that equals K.

We will use iteration boxes of the following form in many of our flowchart examples.

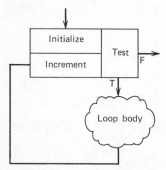

We assume that such boxes are executed in the following order: initialize, test, loop body (if test was true), increment, test, etc., that is, the test is performed immediately after initialization as well as after incrementation (in distinction to the way FORTRAN DO loops are executed). The point 2 in the previous flowchart is supposed to be the point immediately before the test is performed but after the initialization or incrementation step.

Let us first prove that each time execution reaches point 2, $J=0$ and none of the elements $L_1, \ldots, L_{J-1}$ is equal to K.

(i) The first time execution reaches point 2, $J=0$ and $I=1$. The assertion about none of the elements $L_1, \ldots, L_{I-1}=L_0$ is equal to K is trivially true (since there are no such elements).

(ii) Suppose execution is at point 2 and the assertion attached to point 2 is true. Let us call I and J's values at that point I_n and J_n so that we have $J_n=0$ and $1 \leq I_n \leq N+1$, and none of the elements $L_1, \ldots, L_{I_{n}-1}$ is equal to K. If execution proceeds around the loop (from point 2 to 3, to 4 and back to 2), then when execution returns to 2, $J_{n+1}=0$ (since J's value is not changed around the loop) and $I_{n+1} = I_n+1$. If execution proceeds around the loop, we know that the test $I_n \leq N$ is true as well as $1 \leq I_n \leq N+1$ and hence $1 \leq I_n \leq N$. But then when executuion returns to point 2, we would have $1 < 2 \leq I_n+1 = I_{n+1} \leq N+1$ is true. If execution proceeds around the loop and returns to 2 we would also know that the test $K=L_{I_n}$ is false, and hence that none of the elements $L_1, \ldots,$ $L_{I_{n-1}}$ is equal to K and L_{I_n} is also not equal to K. Thus, when execution returns to point 2, none of the elements $L_1, \ldots, L_{I_{n-1}}, L_{I_n} = I_{n+1}-1$ is equal to K. This completes the proof that each time execution reaches point 2, J=0 and $1 \leq I \leq N+1$, and none of the elements $L_1, \ldots,$ L_{I-1} is equal to K.

Since $N \geq 1$, it is apparent that if execution continues to go around the loop, I's value will eventually increase from 1 to N+1. At that point, the test $I \leq N$ would be false and execution would proceed to point 5 and then to point 7 with I = N+1 and J = 0. In this case, we would also know that none of the elements $L_1, \ldots, L_{I-1=(N+1)-1=N}$ is equal to K. The only other way that execution can reach point 7 is from 2, to 3, to 6, to 7. In that case we would know that when execution reaches point 7, $J = I \neq 0$ (since $1 \leq I \leq N+1$) and the test $K = L_I$ was true; hence, $L_I = L_J = K$. We would also know that none of the elements $L_1, \ldots, L_{I-1=J-1}$ is equal to K (since this was true at 2 and I's value is not changed between 2 and 7). This shows that eventually execution will reach point 7, and that when it does, the correctness assertion will be true.

EXERCISES

1. Draw a flowchart that reads in a series of data items (each of which is a real number) one at a time and finds the largest and smallest of these, the total number of data items, and the number that are less than 0. After reading in all the data items and finding these four numbers, the flowchart should print them out and then halt. Prove your flowchart is correct.

2. Given any two positive integers I1, I2, such that I1≤I2, a theorem of mathematics tells us that (the greatest common divisor of I1, I2) GCD(I1, I2) = GCD(I1, I2 - I1) = GCD(I2-I1, I1). Of course, we also know that if I2>0, then GCD(0, I2) = I2. Use

these two facts to prove that the following flowchart correctly computes the GCD(A,B).

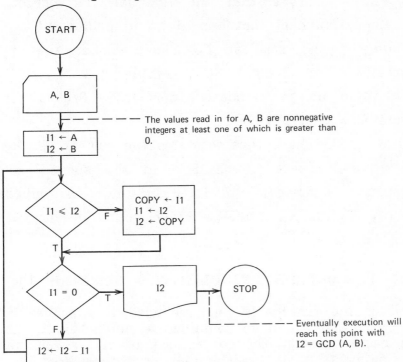

3. Draw a flowchart that finds the largest value in a real valued array X_1, X_2,..., X_N of length $N \geq 1$. Assume the array already has values. Prove the flowchart is correct.

4. Draw a flowchart that searches the array L_1, L_2,..., $L_N (N \geq 1)$ backward (i.e., in the order L_N, L_{N-1}, L_{N-2},..., L_1) for an element that is equal to K. When the flowchart terminates some variable, say J, should be equal to the first subscript in the backward ordering so that $L_J = K$ or 0 if there is no such element. Prove your flowchart is correct.

5. Draw a flowchart that interchanges each of the elements of the array X_1, X_2,..., X_N with the

corresponding elements of the array Y_1, Y_2,..., $Y_N (N \geq 1)$. Prove that the flowchart is correct.

6.   Draw a flowchart that computes and prints out the value of the smallest Fibonacci number that is greater than 5000. See example 1.3.2 for a definition of the Fibonacci numbers. Prove that your flowchart is correct.

7.   Draw a flowchart that computes the sum of all the positive numbers, SUMPOS, and the sum of all negative numbers, SUMNEG, in the real valued array $X_1,...,X_N$ $(N \geq 1)$. Prove your flowchart is correct.

2.4   THE METHOD OF INDUCTIVE ASSERTIONS

All of the flowcharts we have used as examples in Sections 2.2 and 2.3 have contained a single loop. One of the basic steps in the correctness proof for each of these flowcharts was to show that each time execution reaches the loop point, a certain assertion (the loop invariant) is true. In order to show this all we had to show was that (i) the first time execution reaches the loop point the assertion is true and (ii) if execution is at the loop point and the assertion is true, and execution proceeds around the loop and returns to the loop point, then the assertion will again be true. When the control structure of the flowchart becomes more complicated, perhaps involving several nested loops or many alternate paths between key points in the flowchart, it becomes difficult to prove by the above mentioned method that the loop assertions are true each time execution reaches them.

For example, suppose we have a flowchart of the following basic form.

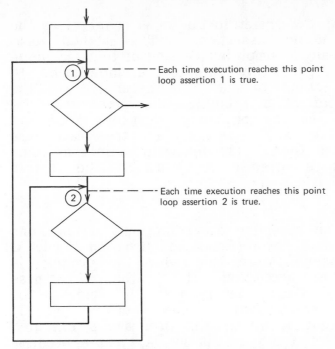

Each time execution reaches this point
loop assertion 1 is true.

Each time execution reaches this point
loop assertion 2 is true.

It may be difficult to apply the above mentioned method to prove either of the two loop assertions. It will probably be straightforward to prove (i) that the loop assertion 1 is true the first time execution reaches point 1. Nevertheless, it may be quite complicated to prove (ii) that if execution is at point 1 and loop assertion 1 is true, and execution proceeds around the loop and returns to point 1, then the assertion is again true. The difficulty is that execution does not proceed around a simple loop and return to point 1. Before returning to point 1 execution proceeds some number of times around the inner loop. Thus we probably need to prove loop assertion 2 first and use it to prove that when execution returns to point 1, loop assertion 1 will again be true. However, in trying to prove that loop assertion 2 is true each time execution reaches point 2, we have a similar difficulty. We really need to show not (i), but (i'), that each time (not just the first time) execution reaches point 2 from point 1, loop assertion 2 is true. To show this, however, we probably need to know that loop assertion 1 is true, which we have not yet proved.

In order to overcome these and similar difficulties, we need to slightly generalize the method of proof we have been using. We refer to this new technique as the method of inductive assertions. The method used previously is really a simplified version of this technique restricted for programs involving only a single loop. In applying the method of inductive assertions to the correctness proof of a program, the proof that the program terminates is completely separated from the proof that certain key assertions are true each time execution reaches them. The following definitions make this notion more precise and are needed before presenting the basic method.

DEFINITION 2.4.1
> Let A be an assertion describing any assumptions about the data for a (flowchart) program and let C be an assertion describing what the program is supposed to accomplish (i.e., the correctness assertion). Then the program is said to be partially correct (with respect to A and C) provided that whenever the program is executed with data satisfying assumption A, if the program terminates then C is true, that is, whenever the program is executed with data satisyfing assumption A, either the program fails to terminate or it terminates with the correctness assertion C being true.

> Thus a program can be partially correct even if it fails to terminate for some (or all) values of the input data that satisfy A. It is only required that for those values of the data that satisfy A and for which the program does terminate, the program accomplishes C.

DEFINITION 2.4.2
> A (flowchart) program is said to be totally correct (with respect to A and C) provided that it is partially correct (with respect to A and C) and terminates for all values of the data that satisfy assumption A.

THE METHOD OF INDUCTIVE ASSERTIONS
> In order to prove that a (flowchart) program is partially correct (with respect to A and C), proceed as follows. Attach the assertion A to the beginning of the

program and attach the assertion C to the terminal point of the program. In addition, discover and attach assertions (which describe relationships concerning the values of the variables) to some other points in the program. In particular, attach such an assertion to at least one point in every closed path (loop) of the program. Then prove for every path in the program leading from a point i, which has assertion A_i attached to it, to a point j, which has assertion A_j attached to it (with no intervening assertions attached to points along the path from i to j), that if execution is at point i and assertion A_i is true, and execution next proceeds from i to j, then when execution reaches point j, the assertion A_j will be true. For a loop the points i and j may be the same point.

To demonstrate that the method does indeed show that the program is partially correct, we prove the following theorem.

THEOREM 2.4.1

If one can carry out the method of inductive assertions for a (flowchart) program, then the program is partially correct (with respect to A and C).

Proof. Suppose we have carried out a proof by the method of inductive assertions and execution of the (flowchart) program is begun with data satisfying assumption A. We wish to show that if the program terminates then C is true. We will actually prove something more general. We will show that each time execution reaches a point in the program that has an assertion attached to it, that the assertion is true. This of course implies that if execution ever reaches the terminal point of the program (and thus terminates), then the assertion C will be true. The proof will be by induction on the number n of points in the program (that have assertions attached to them) that execution execution has reached.

(i) Suppose execution has just reached the first such point, that is, n=1. We need to show that the assertion attached to this point is true. But the first point reached by execution will be the beginning point of the program that has the input assumption A attached to it.

We know this assertion is true, since we are only considering execution of the pgoram with data for which this assertion is true.

(ii)   Suppose execution has just reached some point in the flowchart that has an assertion attached to it, and this is the nth such point that execution has reached. Furthermore, suppose the assertion attached to that point, A_i , is true (this is the induction hypothesis). We need to show that if execution continues from this point to an $n+1^{th}$ point in the program, then the assertion $A_{i_{n+1}}$ attached to that point will also be true. Obviously there must be a path in the flowchart leading from the nth point to the $n+1^{th}$ point. In carrying out the method of inductive assertions for the program, we must have considered this path and shown that if execution is at the nth point and assertion A_{i_n} is true, and execution next proceeds from the nth point to the $n+1^{th}$ point, then when execution reaches the $n+1^{th}$ point, the assertion $A_{i_{n+1}}$ will be true. But this together with the induction hypothesis that A_{i_n} is true when execution is at the nth point implies what we wish to prove, that $A_{i_{n+1}}$ is true when execution reaches the $n+1^{th}$ point.

This completes the proof by induction that if one can carry out the method of inductive assertions for a program, then each time execution reaches a point in the program that has an assertion attached to it, the assertion is true. Thus, if execution ever reaches the terminal point of the flowchart, then the correctness assertion attached to that point will be true, that is, the program is partially correct.

To prove that a program is totally correct first use the method of inductive assertions to prove that it is partially correct and then follow this with a proof that the program terminates. Let us illustrate this technique with several example programs involving nested loops. The reader should attempt to prove the correctness of one of these programs by the earlier restricted method in order to better appreciate the power of the new method.

EXAMPLE 2.4.1

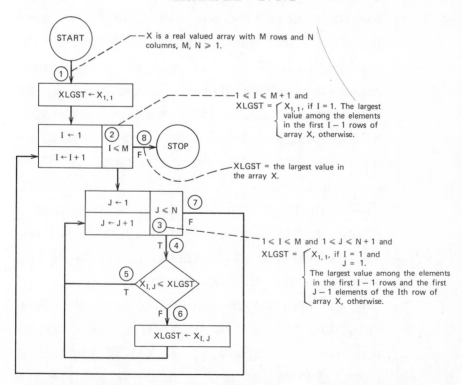

We wish to prove that the above flowchart sets XLGST to the largest value in the array X. The assertions attached to the above flowchart are the inductive assertions needed to prove the partial correctness of the flowchart. Since all of these assertions have the same basic form, namely that each time execution reaches this point the assertion is true, we have deleted from them the repetitious phrase, "each time execution reaches this point." We have not bothered to attach termination assertions to the flowchart, since the proof of termination will be separated from the proof of partial correctness.

   To prove the partial correctness of the flowchart we need to examine each path in the flowchart. Therefore, consider the following.

(i)   The path from 1 to 2. Suppose execution is at 1 and the assertion attached to 1 is true (i.e., the data satisfies this assumption), and execution next proceeds from 1 to 2. We need to show that when execution reaches 2 the assertion attached to 2 will be true. When execution reaches point 2 (from point 1) we will have I = 1 and XLGST = $X_{1,1}$. Since M$\geq$1, we see that 1 $\leq$ I = 1 $\leq$ M+1. Since XLGST = $X_{1,1}$ and I = 1, the assertion about XLGST is also true.

(ii)   The path from 2 to 3. Suppose execution is at 2 and the assertion attached to 2 is true, and execution next proceeds from 2 to 3. We need to show that when execution reaches 3 the assertion attached to 3 will be true. When execution reaches point 3 (from point 2) we will have J = 1 and I and XLGST unchanged from their values at 2. Since N$\geq$1, 1$\leq$J = 1 $\leq$ N+1, and since I's value is unchanged from 2, we will still have 1$\leq$I$\leq$M+1. But if execution proceeds from 2 to 3, we also know that the test I≤M is true, and hence combining this with the fact that 1≤I≤M+1, gives 1≤I≤M. If I = 1 and J = 1, we will have from the assertion at 2, that XLGST = $X_{1,1}$. Otherwise (i.e., I ≠ 1) we will have from the assertion at 2 that XLGST = the largest value among the elements in the first I - 1 rows of array X = the largest value among the elements in the first I - 1 rows and the first J - 1 = 1 - 1 = 0 elements of the Ith row. Thus we see that the assertion attached to 3 will be true when execution reaches 3 (from 2).

(iii) The path from 3 to 4 to 5 to 3. suppose execution is at 3 and the assertion attached to 3 is true, and execution next proceeds along the path 3, 4, 5, 3. We need to show that when execution returns to point 3, the assertion attached to 3 will be true. Let us call the values of I and J when execution is at 3 (before proceeding around the loop) I_n and J_n. Thus we have $1 \leq I_n \leq M$ and $1 \leq J_n \leq N+1$. When execution returns to 3 (by the path 3, 4, 5, 3), $I_{n+1} = I_n$ and $J_{n+1} = J_n+1$. Hence, again, $1 \leq I_{n+1} = I_n \leq M$. If execution proceeds along the stated path, we know the test $J_n \leq N$ is true and, hence, combining this with the fact that $1 \leq J_n \leq N+1$, we have that $1 \leq J_n \leq N$. Thus when execution retuns to 3, we will again have $1 < 2 \leq J_{n+1} = J_n + 1 \leq N+1$. When execution returns to 3, XLGST is unchanged, and we will also know that the test $X_{I_n, J_n} \leq$ XLGST is true. This combined with the truth of the assertion about XLGST before execution proceeds along the path shows that the assertion about XLGST will again be true when execution returns to point 3 with $I_{n+1} = I_n$ and $J_{n+1} = J_n + 1$. For, since $X_{I_n, J_n} \leq$ XLGST, the unchanged value of XLGST will again be the largest value among the elements in the first $I_{n+1} - 1 = I_n - 1$ rows and the first $J_{n+1} - 1 = (J_n + 1) - 1 = J_n$ elements of the I_n^{th} row of array X.

(iv) The path from 3 to 4 to 6 to 3. The argument for this path is identical to that for the previous one except that when execution returns to 3, XLGST's value will have been set to X_{I_n, J_n}. But execution only follows this path provided that the test $X_{I_n, J_n} \leq$ XLGST is false, so that XLGST $< X_{I_n, J_n}$. Thus $X_{I_n J_n}$ is larger than the largest value among the elements in the first $I_n - 1$ rows and $J_n - 1$ columns of the I_n^{th} row, and hence XLGST's new value when execution returns to 3 will again be the largest value among the elements in the first $I_{n+1} - 1 = I_n - 1$ rows and the first $J_{n+1} - 1 = (J_n + 1) - 1 = J_n$ elements of the $I_{n+1}^{th} = I_n^{th}$ row of array X.

(v) The path from 3 to 7 to 2. Suppose execution is at 3 and the assertion attaced to 3 is true, and execution next proceeds from 3 to 7 to 2. We need to show that when execution reaches point 2, the assertion attached to 2 will be true. Execution proceeds from 3 to 7 only if the test $J \leq N$ is false. But we also know from the assertion attached to 3 that $1 \leq J \leq N+1$, and thus we may conclude that $J = N+1$. Let us call the value of I at point 3 I_n. Thus the assertion at 3 tells us that $1 \leq I_n \leq M$ and XLGST = the largest value among the elements in the first $I_n - 1$ rows and the first $J - 1 = (N+1)-1 = N$ elements of the I_n^{th} row of array X. But since there are only N columns in the array, this is the same as XLGST = the largest value among the elements in the first I_n rows of the array X. XLGST's value is not changed between 3 and 2 but I's value is changed to I_n+1. Since $1 \leq I_n \leq M$ is true at 3, this tells us that $1<2 \leq I = I_n+1 \leq M+1$ is true at 2. Also XLGST = the largest value among the elements in the first $I - 1 = (I_n+1)-1 = I_n$ rows of array X will be true when execution reaches 2.

(vi) The path from 2 to 8. Suppose execution is at point 2 and the assertion attached to 2 is true, and execution next proceeds to 8. We need to show that when execution reaches 8, the assertion attached to 8 will be true.

Execution proceeds from 2 to 8 only if the test I≤M is false. But we also know from the assertion attached to 2 that 1≤I≤M+1, and thus we may conclude that I = M+1. XLGST's value is not changed between 2 and 8, and thus the assertion at 2 tells us that when execution reaches 8, we will have XLGST = the largest value among the elements in the first I - 1 = (M + 1)-1 = M rows of array X. But array X only has M rows, and thus this is the same as saying XLGST = the largest value in the array X.

This completes the proof that the flowchart is partially correct. We still need to verify that the flow-chart terminates. Note that the only places where I and J's values are changed in the flowchart are in the incre-mentation compartments of the two iteration boxes. Since J's value is increased by 1 and N's value is un-changed each time execution proceeds around the inner loop (by either path 3, 4, 5, 3 or path 3, 4, 6, 3) J's value must eventually increase to be greater than N. Thus any time execution reaches 3, we know that it will eventually (after some finite number of times around the inner loop) exit to 7 and then to 2. Any time execution reaches point 2, we know that it either goes to 8 and terminates or it proceeds to point 3. If execution proceeds to point 3, we have just seen that it will eventually exit to point 7 and then return to 2. In doing this, I's value gets increased by 1 and M's value is left unchanged. Thus eventually (after doing this some finite number of times) I's value must increase to be greater than M. At that point execution will proceed from 2 to 8 and terminate. This completes the proof of termination and, combined with the previous proof of partial correctness, shows that the flowchart is (totally) correct.

EXAMPLE 2.4.2

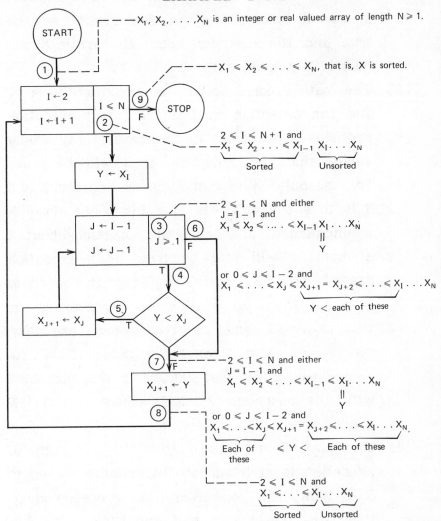

We wish to prove that the flowchart terminates with the array X sorted (into nondescending order).

Let us first prove the partial correctness of the flowchart. So consider the following.

(i) The path from 1 to 2. The student may easily verify that if execution is at 1 and the assertion attached to 1 is true, and execution next proceeds from 1 to 2, then the assertion at 2 will be true. For when execution reaches 2, we will have I = 2, and thus $2 \leq I \leq N+1$ will be true and the assertion about the array X will be trivially true, since I - 1 = 1.

(ii) The path from 2 to 3. If execution is at 2 and the assertion at 2 is true, and execution proceeds from 2 to 3, the reader may easily verify that the assertion at 3 will be true. For the only thing that happens between 2 and 3 is to set $Y = X_I$ and J = I-1. The array X is unchanged, and hence the assertion about X at point 2 will still be true when execution reaches point 3, which is all that is needed to see that the first of the two possibilities for the array X will be true when execution reaches 3. Also, if execution passes from 2 to 3, we will know that $I \leq N$, and this combined with the assertion $2 \leq I \leq N+1$ shows that $1 \leq I \leq N$ will be true at 3.

(iii) The path from 3 to 4 to 5 to 3. Suppose execution is at 3 and the assertion attached to 3 is true, and execution next proceeds along the path from 3 to 4 to 5 and back to 3. Let us call the values of I and J when execution is at 3 (before proceeding along the path) I_n and J_n. Therefore, $2 \leq I_n \leq N$ and either $J_n = I_n - 1$ and $X_1 \leq \dots \leq X_{J_n}$, $X_{I_n} = Y$, $\dots X_N$ or $0 \leq J_n \leq I_n - 2$ and $X_1 \leq \dots \leq X_{J_n} \leq X_{J_n+1} = X_{J_n+2} \leq \dots \leq X_{I_n} \dots X_N$. If execution proceeds along this path, we know

$J_n \geq 1$ is true, and hence $0 \leq J_n - 1$. When execution returns to 3, $I_{n+1} = I_n$ (unchanged) and $J_{n+1} = J_n - 1$. Thus we will still have $2 \leq I_{n+1} = I_n \leq N$ and we will also have $0 \leq J_{n+1} = J_n - 1 \leq I_n - 2 = I_{n+1} - 2$ (regardless of which of the two possibilities was true before proceeding along the path). We will also know that $Y < X_{J_n}$, and the array X will have been changed by setting $X_{J_{n+1}}$ to X_{J_n}. Thus, when execution returns to 3, we will have $2 \leq I_{n+1} = I_n \leq N$ and $0 \leq J_{n+1} = J_n - 1 \leq I_n - 2 = I_{n+1} - 2$ and $X_1 \leq \dots \leq X_{J_{n+1} = J_n - 1} \leq X_{J_{n+1}} = J = X_{J_{n+1} + 2 = J_n + 1} \leq \dots \leq X_I \dots X_N$ (regardless of which of the two possibilities was true before proceeding along the path).

(iv) The path from 3 to 6 to 7. Suppose execution is at 3 and the assertion attached to 3 is true, and execution next proceeds from 3 to 6 to 7. If execution proceeds along this path, then the test $J \geq 1$ is false and hence $J < 1$. This combined with the assertion at 3 tells us that $J = 0$. This means that the second of the two possibilities at 3 must be the true one, since if $2 \leq I \leq N$ and $J = I - 1$, then $1 \leq J$, which contradicts the fact that $J = 0$. But the truth of the second possibility at 3 with $J = 0$ tells us that the second possibility at 7 is also true. In particular, the second possibility at 7 with $J = 0$ becomes $0 \leq J = 0 \leq I - 2$ and $X_{1 = J+1} = X_{2 = J+2} \leq \dots \leq X_I \dots X_N$

The condition about $Y \geq$ each of the elements $X_1, \ldots, X_J$ is trivially true when $J = 0$, since there are no such elements.

(v) The path from 3 to 4 to 7. Suppose execution is at 3 and the assertion at 3 is true, and execution next proceeds along the path from 3 to 4 to 7. If execution proceeds along this path, we know that the test $Y < X_J$ is false or that $X_J \leq Y$. No variables have their values changed along this path. Thus it is easy to see that each of the two possibilities at 3 imply the corresponding possibilities at 7, since $X_J \leq Y$.

(vi) The path from 7 to 8. It is clear that the truth of either assertion at 7 together with setting X_{J+1} to Y will result in the truth of the assertion at 8.

(vii) The path from 8 to 2. Suppose execution is at 8 and the assertion attached to 8 is true, and execution next proceeds from 8 to 2. Let us call the value of I at point 8 I_n. Thus we have $2 \leq I_n \leq N$ and

$$\underbrace{X_1 \leq \ldots \leq X_I}_{\text{sorted}} \underbrace{\ldots X_N}_{\text{unsorted}}$$

When execution reaches point 2, we will have $I = I_n + 1$, and hence, $2 < 3 \leq I = I_n + 1 \leq N+1$ and

$$\underbrace{X_1 \leq \ldots X_{I-1 = I_n}}_{\text{sorted}}, \underbrace{X_{I=I} +1 \ldots X_N}_{\text{unsorted}}$$

(viii) The path from 2 to 9. If execution passes from 2 to 9 then the test I≤N is false and hence N<I. This combined with the fact that 2≤I≤N+1 tells us that I = N+1. But the assertion about the array X at 2 is the same as the assertion about the array X at 9 when I = N+1.

This completes the proof that the flowchart is partially correct. In order to prove that it is (totally) correct, we need to show that execution of the flowchart is guaranteed to terminate. Since I's value is increased and N's value is unchanged each time around the outer loop (and hence I's values must eventually increase to be greater than N if execution keeps returning to 2) and J's value is decreased each time around the inner loop (and hence must eventually decrease to be less than 1 if execution keeps returning to 3, it is apparent to us that execution is guaranteed to terminate.

The above proof has overlooked one important detail. The proof only showed that execution will eventually reach point 9 and that when it does, $X_1 \leq X_2 \leq \ldots \leq X_N$. We really should have shown not only that fact but also that when execution reaches point 9, the values of $X_1, X_2, \ldots, X_N$ are some permutation of their original values, that is, that the original set of values stored in the vector have only been rearranged (without changing the set of values). We left this out of the proof in order to make it less long and tedious. However, you should be able to easily convince yourself of the truth of this assertion (and provide a formal proof of the assertion if necessary).

EXAMPLE 2.4.3

A binary Euclidean Algorithm.

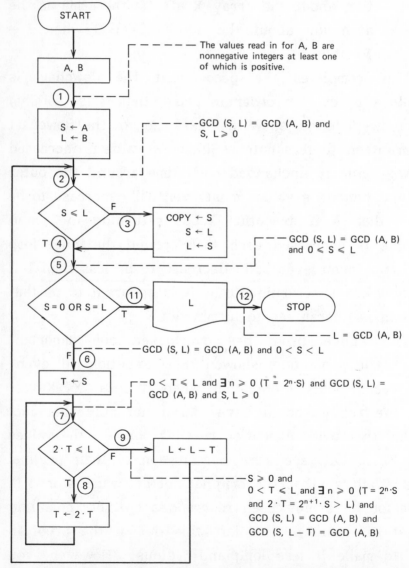

The above flowcart is supposed to compute the the greatest common divisor of A,B (GCD (A,B)) and print

it out. We have attached sufficient inductive assertions
to the above flowchart to allow us to easily carry out an
inductive assertions proof. We wish to leave the details
of that proof to the student. Nevertheless, we would
like to explain how we formulated the inductive
assertions. We knew that the flowchart basically works
by having two variables $0 \leq S, L$ such that at each stage of
execution, GCD (S, L) = GCD(A, B). Each time around
the outer loop, one of the variables S or L has its value
decreased until eventually either S = 0 or S = L. Thus
most of the assertions should be obvious. The assertion
at 2 just states the basic facts about S, L. The assertion at 5 states the same facts about S, L, with the
addition that S<L. But the intervening code between 2
and 5 is designed to assure just this fact, and hence it
should be apparent to the person formulating the assertions. The assertion at 6 is the same as at 5 but with
the stronger condition that 0<S<L. But the falsity of
the test between 5 and 6 assures this and hence should
have suggested it to the person formulating the assertions. Next notice that in passing from 9 back to 2, all
that is done is to set L←L - T. When we get back to 2
it is necessary that GCD(S, L) = GCD(A, B) and S, L>0.
Hence at 9 we had better have that GCD $(S, L-T)$ =
GCD(A, B) and S>0 and $L \geq T$. Thus we need to formulate
enough assertions between 6 and 9 to assure this fact.
Looking at the code between 6 and 9, we see that all it
does is initialize T to S and then double I some number
of times. Hence the assertions about T at 7 and 9
should be fairly obvious. We also observe that between
6 and 9, S, L, A, and B's values are all unchanged,
and hence GCD(S, L) = GCD(A, B) should be true at both
7 and 9, since it is at 6. Thus we hope that the reader
can see fairly easily how each assertion was formulated.

Notice that at 9 we really wrote down more than we
necessarily needed. We saw that we were definitely
going to need that $0 \leq S$ and $0 < T \leq L$ and GCD$(S, L-T)$ =
GCD(A, B). However, in order to prove GCD$(S, L-T)$ =
GCD(A, B), one will probably need the other assertions
attached to 9. In particular the other assertions tell us
that at 9 we have $0 < T \leq L$ and $\exists_n \geq 0$ (T = $2^n \cdot$S and GCD
(S, L) = GCD(A, B)) which imply that GCD$(S, L-T)$ =
GCD$(S, L-2^n \cdot S)$. But it is a fact of mathematics (which
can be proved by induction on M) that for any integer

$M \geq 0$ such that $M \cdot S \leq L$, we have $GCD(S, L - M \cdot S) = GCD(S,L)$. This fact combined with the others at 9 will allow the reader to verify that $GCD(S,L-T) = GCD(S,L) = GCD(A,B)$.

The assertions at 7 and 9 could actually be simplified to the following. At 7 just have that $0 \leq S$, $0 \leq T \leq L$, and $GCD(S,L-T) = GCD(A,B)$. At 9 just have that $0 \leq S$, $0 \leq T \leq L$ and $GCD(S,L - T) = GCD(A,B)$. However, those assertions are less obvious from the structure of the program than the ones we have attached.

We wish to leave the details of the partial correctness proof to the student. The proof of termination of the flowchart is fairly easy. Note that the inner loop is guaranteed to terminate. Since T is initialized to a number $S > 0$. Each time around this loop T is doubled and L is left unchanged. Hence eventually T must increase to be such that $2 \cdot T > L$. In examining the outer loop, we notice that the value of L is decreased by setting $L \leftarrow L - T$ (and we know $0 < T$) before returning to the beginning of the loop. The only other place where either S or L's values could be changed in the outer loop is where S and L's values are interchanged. Hence, each time execution passes around the outer loop starting at 5 and returning to 5, we will have that either S or L's value has been decreased. But we also know that $0 \leq S \leq L$ each time execution reaches this point. We can only decrease either S or L a finite number of times and still maintain the relation that $0 \leq S \leq L$. For eventually one or the other of S or L would be decreased below 0. Thus we see that the outer loop can only be executed a finite number of times before terminating. Note that this proof of termination does not directly prove that execution will eventually reach point 5 with $S=0$ or $S=L$. Instead, it shows that one of the loop invariants can only be maintained for a finite number of times around the loop, and hence execution of the loop must be terminated after some finite number of executions. The use of loop invariants in proving termination is a very useful technique for certain types of flowcharts. Other examples of this technique are pursued in problems 7, 8, and 10 in the following exercises. The method has actually been used implicitly in several of the earlier proofs, for example, the proof of termination for Example 2.3.2 used the loop invariant $0 \leq S$.

EXERCISES

1. Draw a flowchart that computes and prints out the sum of all the elements in an array X that has M rows and N columns. Prove that your flowchart is correct

2.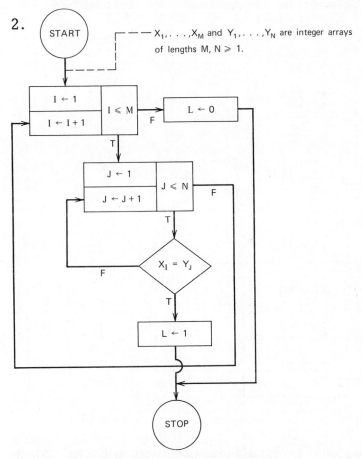

Prove that the above flowchart sets L = 0 if arrays X and Y do not have any values in common and sets L = 1 if they have at least one element in common.

3. Suppose X is an array that has N rows and N columns. Draw a flowchart that checks to see whether or not X is symmetric about its main diagonal. In other words, it checks to see whether or not for all $1 \le I \le N$, $I < J \le N$, $X_{I,J} = X_{J,I}$. The flow-

chart should set some variable to 0 if the array is symmetric and 1 if it is not. Prove that your flowchart is correct.

4.

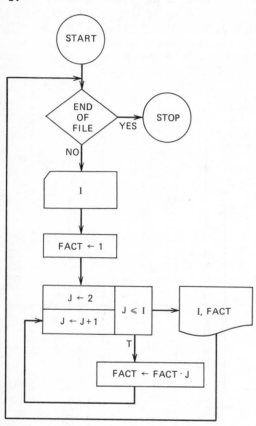

Prove that if this flowchart is executed with an input file consisting of (a finite number of) positive integers, then it will eventually terminate after printing out each number in the input file together with the factorial of that number.

5.   The following flowchart is a version of the straight selection sorting algorithm.

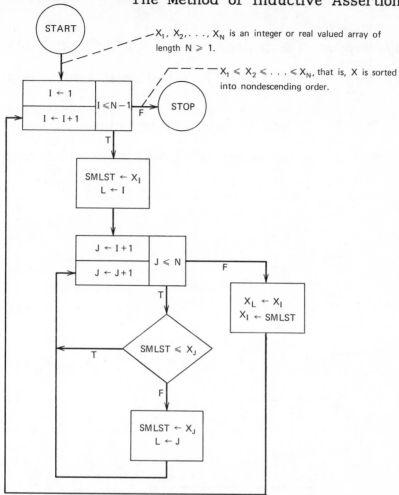

$X_1, X_2, \ldots, X_N$ is an integer or real valued array of length $N \geqslant 1$.

$X_1 \leqslant X_2 \leqslant \ldots \leqslant X_N$, that is, X is sorted into nondescending order.

Prove that the above flowchart is (totally) correct, that is, it terminates with the array X sorted into nondescending order.

6. Suppose that the flowchart in Exercise 5 had been incorrect. For each of the following errors find what step(s) of the correctness proof would fail and then give an example of data for X for which the program would fail.
    (a) Suppose the instruction SMLST←X_I had mistakenly been left out.
    (b) Suppose the instruction L←I had mistakenly been left out.
    (c) Suppose the instruction J←I + 1 had mistakenly

been $J \leftarrow 1$.

(d) Suppose the instruction $J \leftarrow I + 1$ had mistakenly been $J \leftarrow I$.

(e) Suppose the test $J \leq N$ had mistakenly been $J \leq N - 1$.

(f) Suppose the test $SMLST \leq X_I$ had mistakenly had the T and F arrows interchanged.

7.   Prove that the following (skeleton) flowchart terminates.

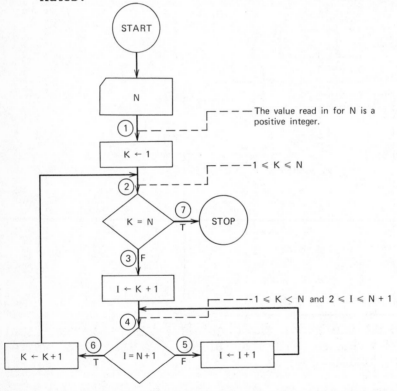

In order to prove that the above flowchart terminates first prove that the assertions attached to points 2 and 4 are true each time execution reaches these points. Using these facts, you should then convince yourself that any time execution reaches point 4, it can only proceed around the loop 4, 5 and back to 4 a finite number of times before exiting this loop and returning to point 2. Next you should show that execution can only pass from point 2 to 4 and eventually back to 2 a finite number of times before K = N is true and execution passes to 7 and terminates.

8. Prove that the following (skeleton) flowchart terminates.

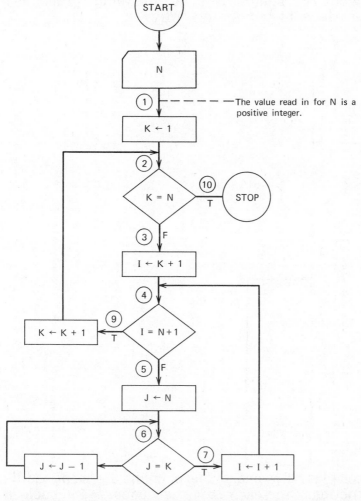

In doing this proof first attach some relevant assertions about the values of the variables at the loop points as in exercise 7 and prove these are true each time execution reaches them. Then use these to prove results about the different loops.

9. In proving termination for complicated flowcharts

(such as Exercise 8) involving several nested or intersecting loops, one must be very careful to check that the value of some variable that determines the termination of one of the loops is not changed in one of the other loops in such a way as to prevent termination. The following (skeleton) flowchart fails to terminate. Why?

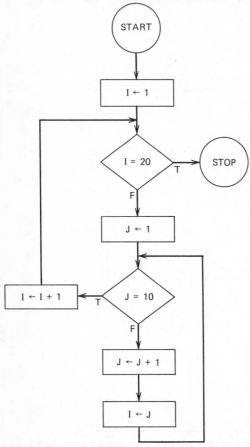

In a complete flowchart there might be many additional instructions in each of the loops. In such a flowchart it is much easier to overlook the fact that some variable is changed in several different loops. Thus one needs to be very careful in proving the termination of such flowcharts.

10. Prove the total correctness of the following flow-chart. Give a careful, detailed argument for the

termination of the flowchart. It may be difficult to prove directly that execution will eventually reach point 2 with I1 = I2. However, you should be able to prove that each time execution reaches point 2 I1>0 and I2>0. You should also be able to prove that execution can only return to point 2 a finite number of times and still maintain this relation.

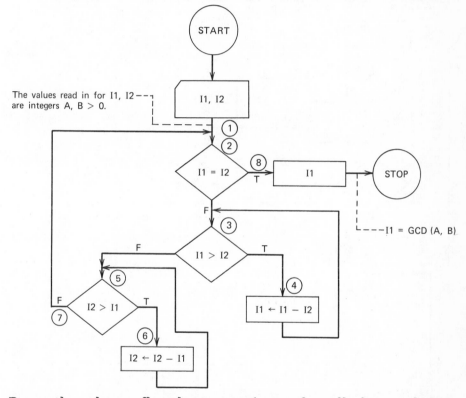

Does the above flowchart terminate for all data values, A,B>0 if the test I1>I2 is changed to I1≧I2. This flowchart is another good example of the use of loop invariants for proving termination.

11. Prove by induction on M that if 0≦S≦L and 0≦M and M·S<L then GCD(S,L-M·S) = GCD(S,L). Then fill in the details of the partial correctness proof for Example 2.4.3.

12. Prove the correctness of the following binary Euclidean algorithm.

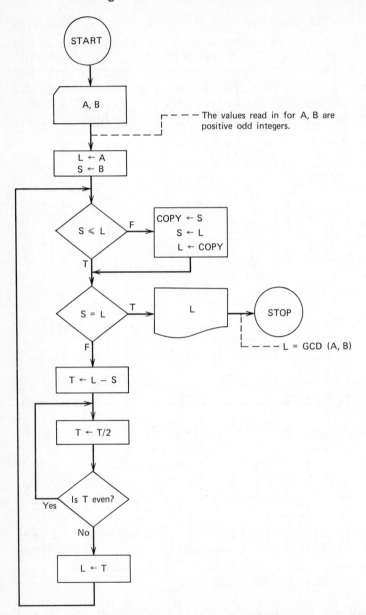

START

A, B

┌ ─ ─ ─ The values read in for A, B are
        positive odd integers.

L ← A
S ← B

S ≤ L   F

COPY ← S
S ← L
L ← COPY

T

S = L   T

L

STOP

L ─ ─ ─ L = GCD (A, B)

F

T ← L − S

T ← T/2

Is T even?
Yes

No

L ← T

2.5 ABBREVIATED CORRECTNESS PROOFS

We believe that the proof that a program is correct should be a standard part of the programming process. Every program should be accompanied by a proof that it is correct. As programmers becomes more experienced with correctness proofs, they will decide to leave out most of the details of the proof. This is perfectly reasonable, since most of the details in such proofs are completely routine. However, as an absolute minimum, we believe that programmers should actually write down, not merely formulate, all of the inductive assertions that are necessary for a proof of the partial correctness of the program. They should then systematically trace all the possible control paths in the program and satisfy themselves concerning the proof for each of these paths, but without necessarily writing down the details of these proofs. They should also verify that execution of the program is guaranteed to terminate, but again wtihout necessarily writing down the details of this proof. We believe that all good programmers essentially desk check their programs in this manner anyway, but with the inductive insertions only vaguely formulated in their minds. We are only trying to make this desk checking a little more systematic by insisting that the programmer consciously formulate and write down the key assertions that describe how the program works and any assumptions about the data. If programmers thoroughly understand their programs, they should, with practice, be able to formulate the necessary assertions and carry out the proofs. If they do not thoroughly understand their programs, the process of formulating and writing down the assertions will be very helpful in forcing them to think carefully about the programs.

We readily acknowledge that an informal, abbreviated correctness proof of the type being discussed here does not really assure one that a program is correct. There can easily be errors (bugs) in such proofs. We do maintain, however, that such proofs are well worth the time spent on them. Since good programmers desk check their programs anyway, we are not really asking them to do anything they do not already do. We believe, however, that by doing this desk checking in the systematic manner of an abbreviated correctness proof, programmers will find the usefullness of this process greatly increased.

2.6 FORMALIZING INDUCTIVE
ASSERTIONS PROOFS

The method of inductive assertions was introduced and illustrated in Section 2.4. The statement of the inductive assertions and the proofs presented in that section were rather informal. One may formalize such proofs by using a more formal notation for stating the inductive assertions and a formal deductive system for carrying out the proofs. This section illustrates some aspects of such a formalization. Some type of formalization of the proofs is necessary if one hopes to ultimately have such proofs carried out, checked, or aided by a mechanical verification system. Readers who are not interested in the topic of formalization may skip this section. The material in this section is not used anywhere else in the book. The most studied formal notation for stating and carrying out mathematical proofs is the notation of the predicate calculus. We assume, for the purposes of this section only, that the student is familiar with this notation.

Recall that the basic method of inductive assertions is as follows. In order to prove that a flowchart is partially correct (with respect to A and C), one attaches the assertion A to the beginning of the flowchart and the assertion C to the terminal point of the flowchart. In addition one must discover and attach to the flowchart some other assertions (which describe relationships that are true concerning the values of the variables each time execution reaches certain points in the flowchart). In particular one must have at least one such assertion attached to some point in every closed path (loop) of the flowchart.   Then one must prove for every path in the flowchart that leads from point i, which has assertion A_i attached to it, to point j, which has assertion A_j attached to it (with no intervening assertions attached along the path from i to j), that if execution is at point i and assertion A_i is true and execution next proceeds along the path from i to j, then when execution reaches point j the assertion A_j will be true.   In order to formalize such proofs we need to:

(i)   Use some formal notation for stating the assertions.

(ii)   Formalize what it is that needs to be proved for each path in the flowchart.

(iii)   Use formal deductive methods to carry out the proof.

The development of formal deductive methods for carrying out proofs is beyond the scope of this book.   The interested reader can pursue that topic in any good text on logic; a particularly good reference is Symbolic Logic and Mechanical Theorem Proving by Chang and Lee (1973).   We will restrict ourselves here to topics (i) and (ii).   (i) can be accomplished by adopting the notation of the predicate calculus (or some other formal notation) for stating all the assertions.   The predicate calculus is not a completely satisfactory notation for stating inductive assertions.   Many inductive assertions are difficult if not impossible to state in that notation.   Finding a

more suitable formal notation for stating inductive assertions and carrying out the proofs is a current research
topic.   Nevertheless,   in   this   section   we   will   use   the
notation of the predicate calculus for stating the assertions.   (ii) can be accomplished by giving a systematic
method   for   generating   for   each   path   in   the   flowchart   a
formalized statement of what needs to be proved for that
path.   The   set   of   all   such   statements   that   need   to   be
proved in order to establish the partial correctness of a
given program is sometimes called the set of verification
conditions for program.

In order to systematically generate the verification
conditions for a flowchart proceed as follows.   Consider
each   of   the   paths   in   the   flowchart.   Suppose   we   are
currently considering a path from point i to point j.   Let
us   symbolize   the   assertion   attached   to   point   i   as A_i
(X,Y,...) where X,Y,... are the variables mentioned in
the   assertion.   Let   us   similarly   symbolize   the   assertion
attached   to   point   j   as A_j (X,Y,...).   Along   the   path
from i to j some variables may have their values changed
by assignment statements.   For   any   variable   V,   let   us
use   the   notation $e_{path}(V)$ (evaluation   of   the   variable
along the path) to stand for the expression that gives
the value of the variable V at point j in terms of the
values   of   the   variables   at   point   i   and   the   values
assigned to the variables by assignment statements along
the path.   For example, if along the path from i to j the
only   assignment   statement   were   X ←Y+1,   then   we   would
have $e_{path}(X)=Y+1$ and $e_{path}(Y)=Y$.   If along this path

there were three assignment statements X←X+1, Y←Y+Y, X←X+ Y-2, then we would have e_{path}(X)=(X+1)+(Y+Y)-2= X+ 2·Y-1 and e_{path}(Y)=Y+Y=2·Y. Along the path from i to j there may also be one or more decision boxes. Let us symbolize the tests in such decision boxes by t_k (X,Y,···). This is supposed to stand for the test that occurs in a decision box at point k in the flowchart and is such that the test depends on variables X,Y,···. Now suppose that t_k(X,Y,···),···,t_l(X,Y,···) is a complete list of all the tests that occur in decision boxes along the path from i to j. For each of these tests t_m(X,Y,···), form a statement t_m^{path} as follows:

$$t_m^{path} = t_m[e_{path'} (X), e_{path'}(Y),···]$$

> If the path from i to j leaves decision box m by the True arrow.

$$t_m^{path} = \sim t_m[e_{path'}(X), e_{path'}(Y),···]$$

> If the path from i to j leaves the decision box m by the False arrow.

> Where path' is the part of the path from i to j that goes from i to decision box m.

Then form the compound statement $C_{path} \equiv t_k^{path} \wedge ··· \wedge t_l^{path}$. The formalized verification condition for the path from i to j is then given by $[A_i(X,Y,···) \wedge C_{path}]$ →A_j (e_{path}(X),e_{path}(Y)···]. If there are no decision boxes along the path from i to j then of course C_{path} should not appear in the statement.

EXAMPLE 2.6.1

Let us reconsider the flowchart discussed in Example 2.2.3. We will use the notation of the predicate calculus for stating the assertions that are attached to the flowchart.

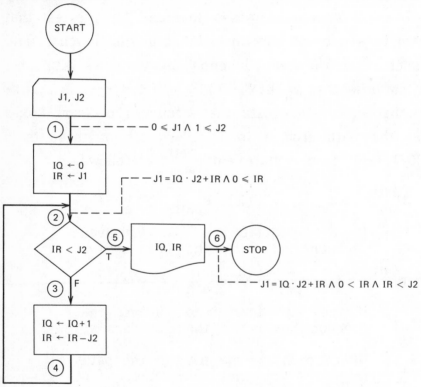

We next generate the set of verification conditions

    (i)   Let us refer to the path from 1 to 2 as path p1. For this path we have $e_{pl}(J1)=J1$, $e_{pl}(J2)=J2$, $e_{pl}(IQ)=0$, $e_{pl}(IR)=J1$. Since there are no decision boxes along this path, the verification condition for this path is

$$(0 \leq J1 \wedge 1 \leq J2) \rightarrow [e_{pl}(J1)=e_{pl}(IQ) \cdot e_{pl}(J2)+$$

$$e_{pl}(IR) \land 0 \leq e_{pl}(IR)]$$

that is $(0 \leq J1 \land 1 \leq J2) \rightarrow (J1 = 0 \cdot J2 + J1 \land 0 \leq J1)$

(ii) Let us refer to the path from 2 to 3, 4 and back to 2 as path p2.

For this path we have $e_{p2}(J1) = J1$, $e_{p2}(J2) = J2$, $e_{p2}(IQ) = IQ+1$, $e_{p2}(IR) = IR-J2$. The only decision box along this path contains the test IR<J2. Let us refer to the (trivial part of path p2 that goes from 2 to this test as path p2'. Since the path p2 leaves this decision box by the False arrow, we have

$$t^{p2} \equiv_\sim [e_{p2'}(IR) < e_{p2'}(J2)]$$
$$\equiv_\sim (IR < J2)$$
$$\equiv J2 \leq IR.$$

Since this is the only decision box along path p2, we have

$$C_{p2} \equiv t^{p2}$$

Thus the verification condition for this path is

$(J1=IQ \cdot J2+IR \land 0 \leq IR \land J2 \leq IR) \rightarrow [e_{p2}(J1) = e_{p2}(IQ)$
$$e_{p2}(J2) + e_{p2}(IR) \land 0 \leq e_{p2}(IR)]$$

that is

$(J1=IQ \cdot J2+IR \land 0 \leq IR \land J2 \leq IR) \rightarrow [J1=(IQ+1) \cdot J2+(IR-J2)$
$$\land 0 < IR-J2]$$

(iii) Let us refer to the path from 2 to 5 to 6 as path p3. For this path we have $e_{p3}(J1) = J1$, $e_{p3}(J2) = J2$, $e_{p3}(IQ) = IQ$, $e_{p3}(IR) = IR$. The only decision box along this path contains the test IR<J2. Let us refer to the (trivial part of

path p3 that goes from 2 to this test as p3'.
We have as before that $e_{p3'}$ (IR)=IR and
e_{p3}'(J2)=J2.   Since the path p3 leaves this
decision box by the True arrow,

$$t^{p3} \equiv e_{p3'}(IR) < e_{p3'}(J2)$$
$$\equiv IR < J2$$

Thus the verification condition for this path is

$$(J1=IQ \cdot J2+IR \wedge 0 \leqq IR \wedge IR < J2) \to (J1=IQ \cdot I2$$
$$+IR \wedge 0 < IR \wedge IR < J2)$$

In order to finish the formalized version of an
inductive assertion proof for this flowchart we
would then need to use formal deductive
methods to carry out the proof of each of the
three verification conditions.   We have not
been willing to take the time to develop such
formal deductive methods in this book but the
student who knows predicate calculus notation
should be able to see that the (formal) proof
of each of the three verification conditions is
essentially trivial, using only basic axioms
about integer arithmetic.

EXAMPLE   2.6.2

Let us reconsider the flowchart that was given as
Exercise 2 at the end of Section 2.3.   Again we will
write the assertions in the notation of the predicate
calculus.

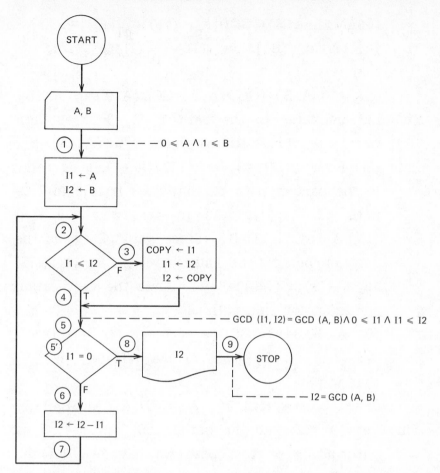

Let us generate the set of verification conditions.

(i)   Let us refer to the path 1, 2, 4, 5 as path p1. For this path we have $e_{p1}(A)=A$, $e_{p1}(B)=B$, $e_{p1}(I1)=A$, $e_{p1}(I2)=B$. Let us refer to the part of path p1 that goes from 1 to 2 as path p1'. For this path we have $e_{p1'}(I1)=A$, $e_{p1'}(I2)=B$. Since path p1 leaves the decision box by the True arrow, we have $t_2^{p1}\equiv e_{p1'}(I1)\leq e_{p1'}(I2)\equiv A\leq B$. Thus the verification condition for this path is

$(0 \leq A \wedge 1 \leq B \wedge A \leq B) \rightarrow \{GCD[e_{p1} (I1), e_{p1}(I2)] = GCD$
$[e_{p1}(A), e_{p1}(B)] \wedge 0 \leq e_{p1}(I1) \wedge e_{p1}(I1) \leq e_{p1}(I2)\}$
that is

$(0 \leq A \wedge 1 \leq B \wedge A \leq B) \rightarrow [GCD(A,B) = GCD(A,B) \wedge 0 \leq A \wedge A \leq B]$

(ii) Let us refer to the path 1, 2, 3, 5 as path p2. For this path we have e_{p2} (A)=A, e_{p2} (B)=B, e_{p2} (I1)=B, e_{p2} (I2)=A. Let us refer to the part of path p2 that goes from 1 to 2 as path p2' (=p1'). As in (i), we have $e_{p2'}$ (I1)=A, $e_{p2'}$ (I2)=B. Since path p2 leaves the decision box by the False arrow, $t_2^{p2} \equiv \sim [e_{p2'}(I1) \leq e_{p2'} (I2)] \equiv \sim (A \leq B) \equiv B < A$. Thus the verification condition for this path is

$(0 \leq A \wedge 1 \leq B \wedge B < A) \rightarrow \{GCD[e_{p2}(I1), e_{p2}(I2)] = GCD$
$[e_{p2}(A), e_{p2}(B)] \wedge 0 \leq e_{p2}(I1) \wedge e_{p2}(I1) \leq e_{p2}(I2)\}$
that is

$(0 \leq A \wedge 1 \leq B \wedge B < A) \rightarrow [GCD(B,A) = GCD(A,B) \wedge 0 \leq B \wedge B \leq A]$

(iii) Let us refer to the path 5, 6, 7, 2, 4, 5 as path p3. For this path we have e_{p3} (A)=A, e_{p3} (B)=B, e_{p3} (I1)=I1, e_{p3} (I2)=I2-I1. There are two decision boxes along this path. The first decision box encountered is at 5'. No variable has its value changed along the path from 5 to 5'. And since path p3 leaves this decision box by the False arrow, we have $t_{5'}^{p3} \equiv \sim (I1=0)$. Let us refer to the part of path p3 that goes from 5 to 2 as path p3'. Along this path we have $e_{p3'}(I1)=I1$, $e_{p3'}(I2)=I2-I1$. Since path p3 leaves the decision box at 2 by

the True arrow, we have $t_2^{p3} \equiv [e_{p3'}(I1) \leq e_{p3'}(I2)]$
$\equiv I1 \leq I2-I1$.   Thus, $C_{p3} \equiv t_{5'}^{p3} \wedge t_2^{p3} \equiv \sim (I=0) \wedge I1 \leq I2-I1$.
Hence the verification condition for this path
is

$[GCD(I1,I2)=GCD(A,B) \wedge 0 \leq I1 \wedge I1 \leq I2 \wedge \sim (I1=0) \wedge I1 \leq$
$\quad I2-I1] \rightarrow \{GCD[e_{p3}(I1), e_{p3}(I2)]=GCD[e_{p3}(A),$
$\quad\quad e_{p3}(B)] \wedge 0 \leq e_{p3}(I1) \wedge e_{p3}(I1) \leq e_{p3}(I2)\}$
that is

$[GCD(I1,I2)=GCD(A,B) \wedge 0 \leq I1 \wedge I1 \leq I2 \wedge \sim (I1=0) \wedge I1 \leq$
$I2-I1] \rightarrow [GCD(I1,I2-I1)=GCD(A,B) \wedge 0 \leq I1 \wedge I1 \leq I2-I1]$

(iv) Let us refer to the path 5, 6, 7, 2, 3, 5 as
path p4.   For this path we have $e_{p4}(A)=A$,
$e_{p4}(B)=B$, $e_{p4}(I1)=I2-I1$, $e_{p4}(I2)=I1$.   The
reader may easily verify that $t_{5'}^{p4} \equiv \sim (I1=0)$ and
$t_2^{p4} \equiv \sim (I1 \leq I2-I1) \equiv I2-I1 < I1$.   Using this information, the reader may easily construct the
verification condition for this path as
$[GCD(I1,I2)=GCD(A,B) \wedge 0 \leq I1 \wedge I1 \leq I2 \wedge (I1=0) \wedge I2-$
$I1 < I1] \rightarrow [GCD(I2-I1,I1)=GCD(A,B) \wedge 0 \leq I2-I1 \wedge I2-$
$$I1 \leq I2-I1]$$

(v) Let us refer to the path 5, 8, 9 as path p5.
For this path we have $e_{p5}(A)=A, e_{p5}(B)=B$,
$e_{p5}(I1)=I1$, $e_{p5}(I2)=I2$.   Thi spath leaves the
decision box 5' by the True arrow.   Thus the
reader can easily construct the verification
condition for this path as
$[GCD(I1,I2)=GCD(A,B) \wedge 0 \leq I1 \wedge I1 \leq I2 \wedge I1=0]$
$$\rightarrow I2=GCD(A,B)$$

The formal proof of each of these five verification conditions would be rather simple. (i) is completely trivial. The other four conditions are simple but, in addition to axioms for integer arithmetic, require axioms that characterize the GCD function. For example, (ii) would require an axiom of the form (X)(Y)[GCD(X,Y)=GCD (Y,X)], (iii) would require an axiom of the form (X)(Y) [0≦X∧X≦Y→GCD(X,Y)=GCD(X,Y-X)]   and   (v)   would require an axiom of the form (Y)[GCD(O,Y)=Y].

EXERCISES

Select some of the flowcharts from the examples or exrcises of Sections 2.2 to 2.4. For each of these, restate the inductive assertions in the notation of the predicate calculus and derive all of the verification conditions.

CHAPTER THREE

PROVING THE CORRECTNESS OF PROGRAMS WRITTEN IN A STANDARD PROGRAMMING LANGUAGE

3.1 INTRODUCTION

The method of inductive assertions discussed in the previous chapter can be applied in a straightforward manner to prove the (partial) correctness of computer programs written in any of the standard programming languages such as FORTRAN, ALGOL, or PL/1. Termination of such programs can also be proved in the same manner as was done previously. In applying the method of inductive assertions one must attach an appropriate assertion to at least one point in each closed control path (loop) of the program. Of course the flow of control in programming languages is implicit in the control structures of the language rather than being explicitly shown (by arrows) as in flowcharts. Thus, in applying the method of inductive assertions to such programs, one must clearly understand the flow of control in the program in order to be sure that one has cut every closed control path in the program. We will concentrate on this aspect of the technique, since the underlying method is identical to that learned in the previous chapter.

In Section 3.2 we illustrate the method for some simple FORTRAN Programs and in Section 3.3 we do the same for some PL/1 programs.

3.2 EXAMPLE CORRECTNESS PROOFS FOR FORTRAN PROGRAMS

EXAMPLE 3.2.1

```
READ (5,1)  J1, J2
```

```
    1 FORMAT (2I10)
C     THE VALUES READ IN FOR J1, J2 ARE TWO INTEGERS
C     SUCH THAT 0 .LE. J1 AND 1 .LE. J2.
      IQ = 0
      IR = J1
    2 IF (IR .LT. J2) GO TO 4
C     J1 .EQ. IQ * J2 + IR AND 0 .LE. IR
        IQ = IQ + 1
        IR = IR - J2
    3   GO TO 2
    4 WRITE (6,5) IQ , IR
    5 FORMAT (2I10)
C     J1 .EQ. IQ * J2 + IR AND 0 .LE. IR AND IR .LT. J2
      STOP
      END
```

The above program is the FORTRAN version of the flowchart previously given in Example 2.2.3. Recall that this program computes the integer quotient IQ and remainder IR of the integer J1 divided by J2. We have inserted as comments the necessary inductive assertions for proving the partial correctness of the program. The comment immediately after the statement labeled 2 is thought of as being attached to the program immediately before the test in this statement, that is, this assertion is supposed to mean that each time execution reaches the point immediately before the test in the statement labeled 2, $J1 = IQ \cdot J2 + IR$ and $0 \leq IR$. Also note that in the proof we use the symbol "=" for equality not assignment.

The proof of partial correctness is then identical to the proof of partial correctness of the corresponding flowchart. Thus we need to consider:

(i) The path from the READ statement to the statement labeled 2. Suppose the READ statement has just been executed and the assertion immediately following it is true, and execution next proceeds to the statement labeled 2. We need to show that the statement immediately following this statement is true. When execution reaches this point, IQ = 0 and IR = J1 and $0 \leq$ J1 and $1 \leq$ J2. Thus it will be true that

$$J1 = IQ \cdot J2 + IR$$
$$= 0 \cdot J2 + J1$$
$$= J1$$

and $0 \leq$ J1 = IR

(ii) The path from the statement labeled 2 down to the statement labeled 3 and back to the statement labeled 2 (the basic loop of the program). Suppose execution is at statement 2 and the assertion below it is true, and execution next proceeds around the loop and back to 2. We need to show that when execution returns to 2, the assertion below it will again be true. Let us call the values of IQ and IR before proceeding around the loop IQ_n and IR_n so that we have $J1 = IQ_n \cdot J2 + IR_n$ and $0 \leq IR_n$. After proceeding around the loop and returning to 2, the values of IQ and IR will be $IQ_{n+1} = IQ_n +$ and $IR_{n+1} = IR_n - J2$, and the values of J1 and J2 will be unchanged. Thus upon returning to 2 we will have

$$IQ_{n+1} \cdot J2 + IR_{n+1} = (IQ_n + 1) \cdot J2 + (IR_n - J2)$$

$$= IQ_n \cdot J2 + J2 + IR_n - J2$$
$$= IQ_n \cdot J2 + IR_n$$
$$= J1$$

Also we know that execution will proceed around this loop only if the test IR_n .LT. $J2$ is false or in other words if $J2 \leq IR_n$. But this tells us that $0 \leq IR_n - J2 = IR_{n+1}$ when execution returns to 2.

(iii) The path from the statement labeled 2 to the statement labeled 4. Suppose execution is at 2 and the assertion immediately below it is true, and execution next proceeds to the assertion labeled 4. We need to show that the assertion below the statement labeled 4 is true. Execution passes from 2 to 4 only if the test IR .LT. $J2$ is true. In passing from 2 to 4 none of the values of the variables are changed and, thus, when execution reaches 4, we will still have that $J1 = IQ \cdot J2 + IR$ and $0 \leq IR$ and, in addition, $IR < J2$.

This completes the proof of partial correctness.

Just as the above proof of partial correctness for this FORTRAN program is for all practical purposes identical to the proof for the corresponding flowchart, the proof of termination would likewise be the same. All that is needed to prove termination for this program is to demonstrate that execution will eventually leave the one loop that this program contains. Hence we only need to show that the test, IR .LT. $J2$, which terminates this loop, is eventually true. But since IR's value is decreased by J2's value each time around the loop and we know J2's value is unchanged, and $1 \leq J2$, we can conclude that IR's value is decreased by at least 1 each time around the loop and thus must eventually decrease to be less than J2.   Thus eventually IR < J2 will be true, and execution will leave this loop and terminate.

EXAMPLE   3.2.2

C1   X IS A REAL VALUED ARRAY OF LENGTH N .GE. 2.

    XSMLST = X(1)

    DO 10 I = 2 , N

C2   XSMLST IS EQUAL TO THE SMALLEST OF X(1),...,X(I-1)

C2   AND 2 .LE. I AND I .LE. N

      IF (XSMLST .LE. X (I)) TO TO 10

      XSMLST = X(I)

C3   XSMLST IS EQUAL TO THE SMALLEST OF X(1),...,X(I-1)

C3   AND 3 .LE. I AND I .LE. N + 1

  10 CONTINUE

C4   XSMLST IS THE SMALLEST OF X(1), ... , X(N)

The above program segment is supposed to set XSMLST equal to the smallest value in the array X(1), ... , X(N).

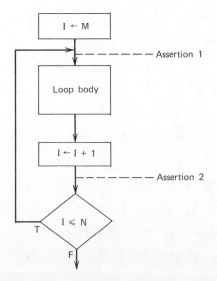

A Fortran DO loop of the basic form:

```
      DO label  I = M, N
C        COMMENT 1
      Loop body
C        COMMENT 2
label CONTINUE
```

has the same flow of control as the flowchart loop shown on the previous page.

The comment 1 that we attach to such a DO loop immediately following the DO statement is thought of as being attached to the same point as assertion 1 in the flowchart and, similarly, the comment 2 that we attach immediately before the end of the DO loop is thought of as being attached to the same point as assertion 2 in the flowchart.

To prove the partial correctness of the program, we then need to consider:

(i)   The path from the beginning of the program fragment to point 2 (the point where comment 2 is attached). At that point of execution, XSMLST = X(1) and I = 2, and hence it is apparent that XSMLST is equal to the smallest of X(1), ... , X(I-1) = X(2-1) = X(1) and that $2 \leq I = 2 \leq N$ (since $N \geq 2$). (Note that we cannot prove this assertion unless $N \geq 2$ and hence the program is not guaranteed to work correctly if N = 1).

(ii) The path from point 2 to point 3 (the point where comment 3 is attached). Suppose execution is at point 2 and comment 2 is true, and I's value at that point is I_n and execution next passes through the loop body to point 2. In the loop body, SXMLST is compared to $X(I_n)$ and, if XSMLST$\leq X(I_n)$, then XSMLST is left unchanged. Otherwise it is set to $X(I_n)$. Since just before that was done we know that XSMLST was equal to the smallest of $X(1)$, ... , $X(I_n-1)$, the student may easily verify that afterward, XSMLST will be the smallest of $X(1)$, ... , $X(I_n)$. But then before execution reaches point 3, I's value is incremented by 1 so that $I_{n+1} = I_n + 1$ and hence again XSMLST will be equal to the smallest of $X(1)$, ... , $X(I_n) = X(I_{n+1}-1)$. Furthermore, from comment 2 we know that $2 \leq I_n \leq N$, and hence it follows that at point 3, $3 \leq I_{n+1} = I_n +1 \leq N + 1$.

(iii) The path from point 3 back to point 2. Execution will follow this path only if the test $I \leq N$ is true. But this fact together with the truth of comment 3 easily leads to the truth of comment 2 when execution reaches point 2.

(iv) The path from point 3 to point 4. Execution follows this path only if the test $I \leq N$ is false, that is, $I > N$. But this together with the truth of comment 3 shows that $I = N + 1$ and, hence, when execution reaches point 4, we will have that XSMLST is equal to the smallest of $X(1)$, ... , $X(I-1) = X[(N+1) - 1] = X(N)$. This completes the proof of partial correctness.

The termination of this program segment is obvious, since it only contains one loop and that is a DO loop.

These two small examples illustrate that the basic technique of inductive assertions can be applied straightforwardly to the correctness proofs of FORTRAN programs. The only difficulties arise from the fact that the flow of control in FORTRAN programs is not as explicit as in flowcharts. This makes it easier to overlook control paths in the program or to misinterpret paths (e.g., by assumming that the DO loop test occurs before execution of the DO loop body). Also, in attaching an inductive assertion to a point in a FORTRAN program, one must be very careful to keep in mind to which (implicit) point one is attaching the assertion. For example, a single FORTRAN statement like a DO statement really corresponds to several different instructions -- counter initialization, counter incrementation, and loop test. In doing the correctness proof one must keep clearly in mind to which of these points the inductive assertion is really attached. The indiscriminant use of GO TO's in FORTRAN programs also presents problems. Programs that use a large number of GO TO's in an undisciplined manner are often difficult to understand and prove correct. This is so because it is very difficult to keep track of all the different control paths through such programs and figure out appropriate inductive assertions along these paths.

The definition and use of subprograms is a very important aspect of programming in FORTRAN and most other high-level programming languages. The method of inductive assertions can be applied rather straightforwardly to prove the correctness of subprograms and programs that call on subprograms. Since we did not deal with such programs in the previous chapter on flowchart programs, we would like to end this section with an example of a correctness proof for a program that calls on a subprogram.

EXAMPLE   3.2.3

```
C      MAIN PROGRAM
       :
       :
C1     0 .LE. I  AND  1 .LE. J  AND  A(I,J)

       CALL  DIV(I, J, K, L)

C2     0 .LE. I  AND  1 .LE. J  AND  A(I,J)
```

C2   AND I .EQ. K*J + L AND 0 .LE. L AND L .LT. J

        :
        :

        END

        :
        :

        SUBROUTINE DIV (J1, J2, IQ, IR)

C3   0 .LE. J1 AND 1 .LE. J2

        IR = J1

    2 IF (IR .LT. J2) GO TO 4

C4   J1 .EQ. IQ * J2 + IR AND 0 .LE. IR

          IQ = IQ + 1

          IR = IR - J2

    3   GO TO 2

    4 RETURN

C5   J1 .EQ. IQ * J2 + IR AND 0 .LE. IR AND IR .LT. J2

        END

In this example we are primarily interested in showing how to deal with subprograms. Consequently, we have not bothered to show a complete main program but have merely indicated a main program that contains a subprogram call. The subroutine DIV is the subprogram version of the program given in EXAMPLE 3.2.1. It is intended to compute the integer quotient and remainder of parameter J1, divided by (parameter) J2 and return these as the values of parameters IQ, IR. The proof that this subprogram works correctly would be identical to the proof given in EXAMPLE 3.2.1. Therefore, suppose the correctness proof for this subprogram has already been carried out and we are working on the correctness proof of the main program. One of the steps in that proof would be to show that if the assertion (C1) immediately before the subprogram call is true and execution passes from that point to the point immediately after the subprogram call, then assertion C2 would be true. In comments C1 and C2, A(I,J) is supposed to stand for some assertion about the variables I and J. In order to carry out the proof for this path, we proceed as follows. Since the actual parameters I, J, K, L are associated by the calling mechanism with the corresponding formal parameters J1, J2, IQ, IR, we should first prove that the assertion C1 implies the assertion at the beginning of the subroutine (C3) provided the parameter names J1, J2, IQ, IR in that assertion are replaced by the corresponding actual parameter names I, J, K, L. In other words, we should prove that C1 implies C3', where C3' is the assertion obtained from C3 by substituting I for J1, J for J2, K for IQ, and L for IR. Thus we need to show that 0 .LE. I and 1 .LE. J and A(I, J) implies that 0 .LE. I and 1 .LE. J. This is obvious. Having done this we of course know that the initial assumptions about the subroutines parameters are valid. Since we assume that we have already done the correctness proof for the subprogram, we do not need to concern ourselves with the internal details of that program. We know that the assertion (C5) attached to the point immediately after the RETURN statement in the subprogram will be true when execution returns to the main program. Of course, this assertion concerns the formal parameters but it will be true of the actual parameters when execution returns to the main program and reaches the point that has assertion C2 attached to it. Thus, in order to see that C2 is true when execution reaches that point, we only need to show that C5' implies C2 where C5' is obtained from C5 by substituting I for J1, J for J2, K for IQ and L for IR. Thus we need to show that I .EQ. K * J + L AND 0 .LE. L AND L .LT. J implies that 0 .LE. I AND 1 .LE. J AND A(I,J) AND I .EQ. K * J + L AND 0 .LE. L AND L .LT. J. The reader may easily verify that C5' does not in fact imply all of C2. C5' only implies the part of C2 that is underlined. How do we verify that the part of C2 that is not underlined is true when execution returns to the point with C2 attached to it? Note that this part of the assertion is identical to the assertion C1. Thus if we knew that the variables I and J, which are the only variables mentioned in C1, where unchanged by the subprogram, then we could conclude that the truth of C1 before the subprogram call implies the truth of the corresponding part of C2 after the subprogram call. Since the actual parameters I, J are associated with the formal parameters J1, J2 of the subprogram, we should examine the subprogram to see if it changes the value of either J1 or J2.   The reader may easily verify that it does not change either J1 or J2.   Thus we are justified in claiming that O .LE. I AND 1 .LE. J AND A(I, J) will still be true when execution reaches the point with C2 attached to it.

The above proof illustrates a general method of proof for dealing with subprograms.   First determine what the subprogram is supposed to accomplish, and prove this by the usual inductive assertions method.   In proving the correctness of a program that calls on one or more subprograms, treat those control paths that involve a subprogram call as follows: First prove that when a subprogram is called upon the assertion at the beginning of the subprogram (which describe any assumptions about the values of the parameters(is true. This was illustrated in the example by showing that C1 implies C3'.   Then show that the assertion attached to the return statement of the subprogram (the correctness assertion for the subprograms) implies the truth of part (or all) of the assertion in the calling program that comes immediately after the subprogram call.   this was illustrated in the example by showing that C5 implies part of C2.   In addition, one may use the fact that any assertions concerning only variables of the calling program that are not changed by the subprogram are still true after returning from the subprogram.   This was illustrated in the example by showing that C1 (which was an assertion of the calling program that involved only variables whose values were not changed by the subprogram) implies the remaining part of C2.

EXERCISES

Write FORTRAN versions of some of the programs given in the examples and exercises of Chapter 2 and prove them correct.   Do a correctness proof for a program that calls on a subprogram.   For example, convert the flow-chart program that computes the greatest common divisor or two integers into a FORTRAN subprogram.   Prove it correct and then prove correct a program segment that calls on it.

3.3 EXAMPLE CORRECTNESS PROOFS
FOR PL/1 PROGRAMS

As with FORTRAN programs the basic method of correctness proofs for PL/1 programs is the same, but we wish to illustrate the use ofsuch methods on programs that use typical PL/1 control structures.

EXAMPLE 3.3.1

```
/*    X(1:N) IS A REAL VALUED ARRAY OF LENGTH 1 < = N */
      SUM = 0.0 ;
      I = 1 ;
      DO WHILE (I < = N) ;
      /* SUM = X(1) +...+ X(I-1) AND 1< = I < = N+1 */
         SUM = SUM + X(I) ;
         I = I + 1 ;
         END ;
/*    SUM = X(1) + ... + X(N) */
```

The above PL/1 program segment is supposed to set SUM = X(1) + ... + X(N). It contains a DO WHILE loop. The meaning of such a loop is that all the instructions between the DO WHILE statement and its corresponding END statement are to be repeatedly executed (0 or more times) as long as the condition in the DO WHILE statement is true. The assertion (comment) that immediately follows the DO WHILE statement is thought of as being attached to the program immediately before the test in the DO WHILE statement, that is, this assertion is supposed to be true each time execution reaches the point just before the DO WHILE test.

The proof of partial correctness for this simple program is straightforward. We need to consider each control path in the program. so consider:

    (i)   The path from the beginning of the program segment to the point just before the test of the DO WHILE statement. Upon reaching this point we will have SUM = 0.0 and I = 1. The assertion that SUM = X(1) + ... + X(I-1) will be trivially true, since $I - 1 = 0$ and as usual we take the empty sum to be 0. Also the assertion that $1 < = I < = N + 1$ is true since $I = 1$ and $N \geq 1$.

(ii) The path from the test of the DO WHILE statement once through the loop and back to the test of the DO WHILE statement. Suppose that before traversing this path, I's value is I_n and the comment is true, that is, $I_n < = N+1$ and SUM $= X(1)+...+X(I_n-1)$. After execution has traversed this path we will have SUM $= [X(1) + ... + X(I_n-1)] + X(I_n)$ and $I = I_n + 1$. Thus it will again be true that SUM $= X(1) + ... + X(I-1)$. Execution will only follow this path provided that the test $I_n < = N$ is true and, hence, upon following this path and returning to the test of the DO WHILE statement, we will again have $1 < = I_n + 1 = I < = N + 1$.

(iii) The path from the test of the DO WHILE statement to the point immediately following the end of the DO WHILE loop. Execution will follow that path only if the test of the DO WHILE statement is false; that is, $I < = N$ is false. But this combined with the fact $1 < = I < = N + 1$ at that point tells us that $I = N+1$. And this fact combined with the fact that SUM $= X(1) + ... + X(I-1)$ tells us that when execution reaches the point immediately after the DO WHILE loop, we will have

$$SUM = X(1) + ... + X((N+1) - 1)$$

$$= X(1) + ... + X(N)$$

which is what we wished to prove.

To prove that the program terminates we only need to show that the DO WHILE loop terminates. But this is obvious since I's value is increased by 1 and N's value is left unchanged each time around the loop. Thus I's value must eventually increase to be greater than N, and hence the test $I < = N$ will eventually be false.

EXAMPLE 3.3.2

```
/*     M, N  ALREADY HAVE INTEGER VALUES AND 0 < = N */
       I = 1 ; J = M ; K = N ;
       DO WHILE (K  = 0) ;
       /*  I * (J * * K) = M * * N AND 0 < = K  */
          DO WHILE (MOD (K, 2) = 0) ;
          /*  I * (J * * K) = M * * N AND 0 < K  */
             K = K / 2E0 ;
             J = J * J ;
             END ;
          K = K - 1 ;
          I = I * J ;
          END;
/*     I = M * * N  */
```

We wish to prove that the above PL/1 program computes and sets I to M * * N. To prove the partial correctness of the above program segment, consider:

(i)   The path from the beginning of the program segment to the point just before the test of the outer DO WHILE statement. When execution reaches this point we will have I = 1, J = M and K = N and thus I * (J * * K) = 1 * (M * * N) = M * * N. We will also have 0 < = N = K. Thus the assertion attached to the point just before the test of the outer DO WHILE statement will be true.

(ii)   The path from the test of the outer DO WHILE statement to the test of the inner DO WHILE statement.   Nothing happens along this path except that we determine that $K \neg = 0$.   Hence the assertion attached to the inner DO WHILE statement must be true.

(iii) The path from the test of the inner DO WHILE statement once around the inner DO WHILE loop and back to the test of the inner DO WHILE statement.   Suppose that just before execution follows this path, $I = I_n$, $J = J_n$ and $K = K_n$.   Then we know that $I_n * (J_n * * K_n) = M * * N$ and $0 < K_n$.   Furthermore, if this path is followed, we must have MOD $(K_n, 2) = 0$, that is, K_n is divisible without remainder by 2.   After going around this loop once, we will have $I = I_n$, $K = K_n/2E0$ and $J = J_n * J_n$. Thus we will have

$$I*(J * * K) = I_n * [(J_n * J_n) * * K_n/2]$$
$$= I_n * ((J_n * * K_n/2E0) * (J_n * * K_n/2E0)$$
$$= I_n * (J_n * * (K_n/2E0 + K_n/2E0)$$
$$= I_n * (J_n * * K_n) \text{ since } K_n \text{ is divisible without remainder by 2}$$

$$= M * * N$$

Furthermore, since $0 < K$ and K is divisible without remainder by 2, we must have $K = K_n/2E0 > 0$.   Thus the assertion attached to the inner DO WHILE statement will again be true when execution returns to the DO WHILE statement.

(iv) The path from the test of the inner DO WHILE

statement to the end of the outer DO WHILE loop and back to the (test of the) outer DO WHILE statement. So suppose execution is at the inner DO WHILE statement and $I = I_n$ and $J = J_n$ and $K = K_n$. At this point we have $I_n *$ $(J_n * * K_n) = M * * N$ and $0 < K_n$. Furthermore, if execution follows this path, it must be because the test of the inner DO WHILE loop is false, that is, $MOD(K_n, 2) = 0$ is false. Upon passing to the end of the outer DO WHILE loop and returning to the test of the outer DO WHILE statement we will have $K = K_n - 1$, $I = I_n * J_n$ and $J = J_n$. Thus at that point we would have

$$
\begin{aligned}
I * (J * * K) &= (I_n * J_n) * [J_n * * (K_n-1)] \\
&= I_n * [J_n * (J_n * * (K_n-1)] \\
&= I_n * [J_n * * [1 + K_n - 1]] \\
&= I_n * (J_n * * K_n) \\
&= M * * N
\end{aligned}
$$

Furthermore, since $0 < K_n$, we would have $0 < K_n - 1 = K$. Thus the assertion attached to the outer DO WHILE statement will again be true.

(v) The path from the (test of the) outer DO WHILE loop to the point just past the end of the outer DO WHILE loop. If execution follows this path we know the test $K \neg = 0$ is false, that is, $K = 0$. Also the assertion attached to the outer DO WHILE statement is true, that is

I * (J * * K) = M * * N. But this implies that when execution leaves the outer DO WHILE loop,

$$I * (J * * K) = I * (J * * 0)$$
$$= I * (1)$$
$$= I$$
$$= M * * N$$

This is what we wished to prove.

In order to prove the termination of this program we need to show that both DO WHILE loops terminate each time they are entered. To see that the inner DO WHILE loop is guaranteed to terminate, notice that each time around this loop, K is set to K/2E0. Thus it has a factor of 2 removed from it. Hence eventually K must be reduced to the point where it is not divisible without remainder by 2. At that point the test MOD(K,2) = 0 will be false. To see that the outer DO WHILE loop is gauranteed to terminate, note that each time around the outer DO WHILE loop, K's value is decreased by at least 1. If execution passes around the inner DO WHILE loop one or more times, then K is decreased by some power of 2. Even if execution does not pass around the inner DO WHILE loop, K is set to K - 1 before reaching the end of the outer DO WHILE loop. Thus in any case K's value is decreased by at least 1 each time around the outer DO WHILE loop. Since we also know 0 < = K, this tells us that K's value must eventually decrease to be 0. At that point the test K = 0 will be false, and the outer DO WHILE loop will terminate.

3.4   AN AXIOMATIC TREATMENT OF PARTIAL CORRECTNESS

We have presented partial correctness proofs for programs written in a programming language in essentially the same style as we used for flowchart programs. That is, we have done such proofs by attaching inductive assertions to certain key points in the programs. In particular there has to be at least one such assertion attached to some point along every closed control path (loop) through the program.   We then show that each time execution reaches a point with an assertion attached to it, the assertion is true.   Such partial correctness proofs for programs can be presented in a slightly different notation.   They can be presented as being based upon certain axioms or verification rules.   In this section we wish to familiarize students with such verification rules and allow them to see their equivalence with the method of inductive assertions.   We will not give a complete set of such verification rules for some programming language but merely illustrate the idea with a couple of examples.   We use the following notation for presenting such verification rules: $\{A_1\}$ P $\{A_2\}$, where A_1 and A_2 are (inductive) assertions and P is a program segment consisting of one or more instructions.   The notation means that if assertion A_1 is true immediately before execution of program segment P and if execution of P terminates, then A_2 will be true immediately after execution of P.   Using this notation we can then present a couple of examples of verification rules.

EXAMPLE   3.4.1

Suppose the programming language we are using has an instruction of the form IF C THEN S1 ELSE S2 and we wish to prove (as part of a partial correction proof) that $\{A_1\}$ IF C THEN S1 ELSE S2 $\{A_2\}$, that is we wish to prove that if assertion A_1 is true immediately before execution of the above instruction and execution of the instruction terminates, then assertion A_2 will be true immediately after execution of the instruction.   We assume the instruction has the usual meaning in this programming language, that is, it is equivalent to the flowchart fragment shown below.   An axiom or verification rule that one may use in proving the above is the following:
If one can prove that

      (i) $\{A_1$ AND C$\}$ S1 $\{A_2\}$
and (ii) $\{A_1$ AND NOT C$\}$ S2 $\{A_2\}$
then one may conclude the desired result that
      (iii) $\{A_1\}$ IF C THEN S1 ELSE S2 $\{A_2\}$
The equivalence of this axiom with the method of inductive assertions as presented in this book should be apparent, since, in proving the partial correctness of

the corresponding flowchart fragment:

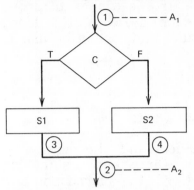

we would have to verify that:

(i') If execution is at point 1 and assertion A_1 is true, and execution next passes from 1 to 3 to 2, then assertion A_2 will be true. But for this path we know that both A_1 is true and the test C is true before S1 is executed. We have to show that if execution reaches 2 (i.e., execution of S1 terminates) then A_2 is true.

(ii') If execution is at point 1 and assertion A_1 is true, and execution next passes from 1 to 4 to 2, then assertion A_2 is again true. But, for that path, we know that both A_1 is true and the test C is false (NOT C is true) before S2 is executed. We have to prove that if execution reaches 2 (i.e., execution of S2 terminates, then A_2 is true.

Thus the two results, (i') and (ii'), that we need to verify for the method of inductive assertions are essentially identical to the two preconditions, (i) and (ii), that we must prove in order to use the verification rule.

EXAMPLE 3.4.2

Suppose the programming language we are using has an instruction of the form:

    DO WHILE (C);

        S

    END;

We assume the instruction has the usual meaning in this

programming language, that is it is equivalent to the flowchart fragment shown below. If one wishes to prove that $\{A_1\}$ P $\{A_2\}$ where P is such a DO WHILE loop, then an axiom or verification rule that one may use is the following:

If one can prove that

    (i) $\{A_1 \text{ AND } C\}$ S $\{A_1\}$

    (ii) A_1 AND NOT C imply A_2

then one may conclude the desired result that

    (iii) $\{A_1\}$ P $\{A_2\}$

Again the equivalence of this axiom and the method of inductive assertions should be apparent, since in proving the partial correctness of the corresponding flowchart fragment:

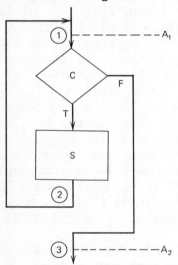

we would have to verify that:

    (i') If execution is at point 1 and assertion A_1 is true, and execution next passes from 1 to 2 and back to 1, then assertion A_1 will again be true. But for this path, we know that both A_1 is true and the test C is true before S is executed. We have to show that if execution returns to 1 (i.e., execution of S terminates), then A_1 is true.

    (ii') If execution is at point 1 and assertion A_1 is true, and execution next passes from 1 to 3, then assertion A_2 will be true. But along this path we will have that both A_1 is true and C is false (i.e., NOT C is true). Thus for this path, we have to show that A_1 and not C, imply A_2.

Thus the two results, (i') and (ii') that we need to verify for the method of inductive assertions are essentially identical to the two preconditions, (i) and (ii), that we must prove in order to use the verification rule.

The above verification rule is sometimes written in the less general form:

If one can prove that

(i)   {A_1 AND C} S {A_1}

then one may conclude that

(ii)   {A_1} P {A_1 AND NOT C} (where P is a DO WHILE loop)

The reader should easily be able to justify this version of the rule. The reader should also notice that each of these rules is only to be used to prove partial correctness. The successful use of such rules does not imply that P terminates.

EXAMPLE 3.4.3

We wish to give an example of a partial correctness proof using verification rules. In order to do so we need one more verification rule. Suppose P1 and P2 are two program segments and we wish to prove something about the program segment that consists of P1 followed by P2. The following verification rule may be useful in such a proof.

If one can prove that

(i)   {A_1} P1 {A_2}

and

(ii)   {A_2} P2 {A_3}

then one may conclude that

(iii) {A_1} P1; P2 {A_3}

In the following proof we use the alternative notation:

{A_1}

  P

{A_2}

to mean the same thing as

{A_1} P {A_2}

The program we wish to prove correct using verification rules is the PL/1 version of the flowchart program proved correct in EXAMPLE 2.2.3. The reader should compare these two proofs and see that they are essentially identical.

```
/* {0≦J1 AND 1 ≦ J2} */
IQ = 0 ;
IR = J1 ;
/* {J1 = IQ·J2 + IR AND 0 ≤ IR} */
DO WHILE (IR ≥ J1) ;
    IQ = IQ + 1 ;
    IR = IR - J2 ;
END ;
/* {J1 = IQ·J2 + IR AND 0 ≤ IR < J1} */
```

We wish to prove that $\{0{\leqq}J1$ AND $1 \leqq J2\}$ P $\{J1 = IQ{\cdot}J2 + IR$ AND $0{\leqq}IR{<}J1\}$ where P is the above program segment. In order to do so, we need to prove:

(i) $\{0 \leqq J1$ AND $1 \leqq J2\} \equiv \{A_1\}$

   IQ = 0 ;

   IR = J1 ;

   $\{J1 = IQ{\cdot}J2 + IR$ AND $0 \leq IR\} \equiv \{A_2\}$

   But this is apparent, for, after the two instructions of the program segment are executed, we will have IQ = 0 and IR = J1, and therefore $J1 = 0{\cdot}J2 + J1 = J1$ is true and since $0{\leqq}J1$ is true before the instructions are executed and J1's value is not changed by the instructions we will have $0{\leqq}J1{=}IR$ is true after the instructions are executed.

(ii) $\{J1 = IQ{\cdot}J2 + IR$ AND $0 \leq IR\} \equiv \{A_2\}$

   DO WHILE (IR ≥ J1) ;

       IQ = IQ + 1 ;

       IR = IR - J2 ;

END;

$\{J1 = IQ \cdot J2 + IR \text{ AND } 0 \leq J1\} \equiv \{A_3\}$

In order to prove this we will use the verification rule given in Example 3.4.2. That verification rule allows us to conclude the above, provided that we can prove:

(a) $\{A_2 \text{ AND } IR \geq J1\}$

   IQ = IQ + 1; ;

   IR = IR - J2 ;

   $\{A_2\}$

Therefore, suppose the values of the variables before this program segment is executed are $J1_n$, $J2_n$, IQ_n, and IR_n. Thus we may assume that $J1_n = IQ_n \cdot J2_n + IR_n$ and $0 \leq IR_n$ AND $IR_n \geq J1_n$. After the program segment is executed the values of the variable will be $J1_{n+1} = J1_n$, $J2_{n+1} = J2_n$, $IQ_{n+1} = IQ_n + 1$, and $IR_{n+1} = IR_n - J2_n$. We need to show that $J1_{n+1} = IQ_{n+1} \cdot J2_{n+1} + IR_{n+1}$ and $0 \leq IR_{n+1}$. But this follows easily as may be verified by substituting the values of $J1_{n+1}$, $J2_{n+1}$, IQ_{n+1}, and IR_{n+1} into the statement. For, upon substituting these values, we have

$$J1_n = (IQ_n + 1) \cdot J2_n + (IR_n - J2_n)$$
$$= IQ_n \cdot J2_n + J2_n + IR_n - J2_n$$
$$= IQ_n \cdot J2_n + IR_n$$

and

$$0 \leq IR_n - J2_n$$

or

$$J2_n \leq IR_n$$

both of which were assumed to be true.

(b) A_2 and NOT $(IR \geq J1)$ imply A_3; that is, $J1 = IQ \cdot J2 + IR$ AND $0 \leq IR$ and NOT $(IR \geq J1)$ imply $J1 = IQ \cdot J2 + IR$ AND $0 \leq IR < J1$.   But this is obvious since $J1 = IQ \cdot J2 + IR$ implies $J1 = IQ \cdot J2 + JR$ and $0 \leq IR$ and NOT $(IR \geq J1)$ implies $0 \leq IR < J1$.

We now have proved that

(i) $\{A_1\}$

IQ = 0;

IR = J1;

$\{A_2\}$

(ii) $\{A_2\}$

DO WHILE $(IR \geq J1)$;

    IQ = IQ + 1 ;

    IR = IR - J2;

END

$\{A_3\}$

and, therefore, by the verification rule stated at the beginning of this section, we may conclude the desired result:

(iii) $\{A_1\} = \{0 \leq J1$ AND $1 \leq J_2\}$

IQ = 0 ;

IR = J1 ;

DO WHILE $(IR \geq J1)$;

    IQ + IQ + 1 ;

    IR = IR - J2 ;

END ;

$$\{A_3\} \equiv \{J1 = IQ \cdot J2 + IR \text{ AND } 0 \leq IR < J1\}$$

The reader should be able to see that this proof using verification rules is essentially identical to the proof that would be given using the method of inductive assertions.

EXERCISES

1. Suppose the programming language we are using has an instruction of the form IF C THEN S, and we wish to prove that $\{A_1\}$ IF C THEN S $\{A_2\}$. Formulate a verification rule for use with such an instruction.

2. Suppose the programming language we are using has an instruction of the form REPEAT S UNTIL C. We assume the instruction has the usual meaning in this programming language, that is, it is equivalent to the flowchart fragment shown below. Formulate a verification rule for use in trying to prove $\{A_1\}$ REPEAT S UNTIL C $\{A_2\}$.

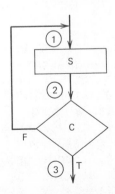

3. Suppose we wish to show that
$$\{A_1\}$$

```
      DO WHILE (C1) ;
          IF C2 THEN S1 ELSE S2 ;
      END ;
      {A₂}
```

State exactly what would have to be proved in order to use the verification rules of Examples 3.4.1 and 3.4.2 to show this result.

4.   Prove that the following PL/1 program segment is partially correct by the use of verification rules.

```
/*{0 ≤ N} */
   I = 0 ;
   J = 1 ;
   DO WHILE (I < N) ;
       J = J * M ;
       I = I + 1 ;
   END ;
/* {J = M**N} */
```

3.5   PROVING PROGRAM CORRECTNESS AS PART OF THE PROGRAMMING PROCESS

All of the example proofs of program correctness in this book have dealt with completed (and small) programs. However, in practice, such proofs should be given by the programmer during the programming process. One should not expect to take a large, finished program and prove it correct. The intellectual demands of such a proof are likely to be too great. One must prove the correctness of small sections of code as they are completed. In order to do this, the sections of code must not be unnecessarily interrelated by a "spaghetti bowl" control structure. Many people have suggested that programmers can avoid unnecessarily complicated, interrelated control structures by avoiding

the use of GO TO's and restricting themselves to some
small set of one-in, one-out control structures such as
(1) sequencing, (2) conditional branching of the basic
form IF C THEN S1 ELSE S2, and (3) repetitive con-
structions of the basic form WHILE C DO S.
Programs written in this style are frequently called
"structured" programs. Nevertheless, the restriction to
such a subset of control structures is certainly no
cure-all. It is just as possible to write murky, difficult
to verify programs using these control structures as it
is with control structures that make use of some GO
TO's. What is important is that the program be clearly
conceived and rendered with a control structure that
does not unnecessarily interrelate sections of code (by
jumping back and forth using GO TO's).

In verifying the correctness of a larger section of
code, several of whose subsections have already been
verified, one can treat such subsections as if they were
single (abstract) instructions whose execution results in
the truth of a postcondition assertion (the correctness
assertion for that subsection) provided that some precondition assertion (the input assertion for that subsection) is true before the subsection is executed.
Thus, in verifying the correctness of the larger section,
one does not necessarily have to look inside the subsections. The process is often done in the reverse
order, that is, one writes (in a top-down manner) the
code for the larger section leaving some of its subsections unspecified for the moment. In proving the
correctness of the larger section one then assumes that
the subsections will be written so that their execution
results in the truth of some postcondition assertion,
provided that some precondition assertion is true before
execution of the subsection. Based on those assumptions
one then proceeds to verify the larger section of code.
Later when one codes a subsection, the correctness
proof for the subsection must consist of showing that if
the assumed precondition assertion is true before
execution of the subsection then the assumed postcondition assertion will be true after its execution.

As we stated at the end of Chapter 2, we do not
believe that programmers necessarily need to write down
all of the details of the correctness proofs. We do
believe, however, that they should, as a minimum, write

down the key assertions (as comments) and then carefully verify for themselves they are true (but without
writing down all the details of the proofs).   They should
also carefully verify that the program terminates, but
again without necessarily writing down all the details of
the proof.

The main point of this section is that these informal
correctness proofs should be given during the programming process, not after the whole program is complete.

EXERCISES

Write a computer program in the programming language
of your choice for each of the following problems. Prove
your program is correct.

1.   Suppose integer arrays X(1:M) , Y(1:N) are sorted
     in ascending order [i.e., no repetitions and X(1) <
     X(2) ... <X(M) . Y(1) < Y(2) < ... < Y(N)].
     Develop a program that will produce and print out
     two arrays, UNION (1:L1), INTERSECTION (1:L2),
     that are as follows: UNION (1:L1) contains in
     ascending order (without repetitions) all elements
     that are in either X(1:M), or Y(1:N), or both.
     INTERSECTION (1:L2) contains in ascending order
     (without repetitions) all elements that are in both
     X(1:M) and Y(1:N).

2.   Develop a program that takes as input any positive
     integer and tests that number to see if it is a
     perfect number.   An integer N is a perfect number
     if and only if it is the sum of all integers I such
     that $1 \leq I < N$ and I divides N without remainder.
     For example, 6 is a perfect number since 6 = 1 +
     2 + 3.

3.   Suppose we have an integer array X(1:N) that we
     wish to sort.   The best general purpose sorting
     algorithms have execution times porportional to N ·
     Log N.   However, if we know that the array con-
     tains only a few different values, we should be able
     to design a special purpose sorting algorithm that
     has an executime proportional to N.
     (a) Suppose X(1:N) contains only the values 1 and
          2. Develop an interchange type sorting pro-
          gram [i.e., a program in which the only way
          the value of an element X(I) can be changed is
          by interchaning it with some element X(J), and

where counting the number of elements of each type is illegal] that will sort X(1:N) in time proportional to N while making only one pass through the array.

(b) The same as (a) except that the array may contain values 1, 2, and 3.

4.   Suppose we have an array X(1:N) whose values are some permutation of the integers 1 to N. Develop an interchange type sorting algorithm that will sort the array with at most N interchanges and execution time that is proportional to N.

5.   Develop a program that can test any sequence of integers of length ≤ N to see whether any immediately adjacent pair of subsequences (of length 1 or greater) are equal. For example, 3 1 <u>2</u> <u>2</u> 4 and 1 <u>3 5 2</u> <u>3 5 2</u> 7 8 both have a pair of immediately adjacent subsequences that are equal. 1 3 5 2 3 5 does not have any such pair.

6.   Develop a program to generate and print out all permutations of 1 2 3 . . . N in lexicographic order.

7.   Develop a program that generates and prints out in ascending order the smallest N elements in the sequence 1, 2, 3, 4, 6, 8, 9, 12, 16, 18, ... This sequence is defined by the rule that:

(i)   1 is the first element of the sequence.

(ii)   If s is in the sequence then so is 2·s and 3·s.

(iii) No number is in the sequence except those determined by (i) and (ii).

CHAPTER FOUR

PROVING THE CORRECTNESS OF RECURSIVE PROGRAMS

4.1 INTRODUCTION

Many programming languages (e.g., ALGOL, PL/1, LISP) allow the programmer to write recursive programs; that is, programs that as part of their computation call upon themselves (recursively) just as a nonrecursive program might call upon a subprogram. Such recursive programs are particularly useful in dealing with recursively defined data structures such as lists or trees. Thus recursion is fundamental in a language such as LISP, which is primarily designed for doing nonnumerical computations involving lists. In this chapter we deal with the methods that are useful in proving the correctness of such recursive programs. The basic method we employ in such proofs is called structural induction. Structural induction proofs are proofs by mathematical induction where the induction is upon the structure of the data manipulated by the program.

The student who is unfamiliar with recursion should still be able to follow the material here. We do not use any of the standard (recursive) programming languages, such as ALGOL or LISP, but instead invent a simplfified programming language that is sufficient for illustrating recursion. This language is explained in Section 4.2. The basic method of structural induction is explained in Section 4.3 and further illustrated in Section 4.4. In Section 4.5 we show that the method of structural induction is sometimes useful even in dealing with nonrecursive programs. In particular, we illustrate how the method of structural induction is sometimes easier to use than the method of inductive assertions for proving the correctness of a nonrecursive programs that are essentially carrying out recursive processes, such as traversing a tree.

4.2   A SIMPLIFIED PROGRAMMING LANGUAGE
FOR ILLUSTRATING RECURSION

We wish to use a simplified programming language for illustrating recursion.   The reader who is familiar with recursion in an actual programming language, such as ALGOL or LISP, can easily relate this simplified language to the corresponding recursive aspect of the actual language.   Nevertheless, the reader who is unfamiliar with recursion in an actual language should still be able to understand the material in this section.

Each program in our simplified programming language will consist of the definition of a function in the following form:

$$F(X1, \cdots, XN) \equiv \text{IF test 1 THEN expression 1}$$
$$\text{ELSE IF test 2 THEN expression 2}$$
$$\vdots$$
$$\text{ELSE IF test m THEN expression m}$$
$$\text{ELSE OTHERWISE expression m+1}$$

The basic meaning of such a program is that to compute the value of $F(X1, \cdots, XN)$ one first performs test 1 and, if test 1 is true, then the value of the function is the value of expression 1.   If test 1 is false then one next performs test 2 and, if test 2 is true, then the value of the function is the value of expression 2.   One continues in this manner until one finds the first test i that is true.   The value of the fucntion is then the value of expression i.   If none of the tests is true then the value of the function is the value of the expression m+1. Recursion enters into this programming language by allowing the function F, which is being defined by the program to occur as a part of any of the expressions or tests of the program.   Such an occurrence of F is referred to as a recursive call of the function.   For each such recursive program one must also state for what values of the arguments $X1, \cdots, XN$ the program applies, that is, one must state what the domain of the function is.   Execution of the program then consists of applying the program to some particular data in the domain of the function.

EXAMPLE 4.2.1
Consider the following recursive program that is applicable to any positive integer X.

$$F(X) \equiv IF \ \ X = 1 \ \ THEN \ 1$$

$$ELSE \ OTHERWISE \ X \cdot F(X-1)$$

To understand more clearly how recursion works let us follow the execution of this program for some particular value of the argument X.   For example,

$F(4)$	$= \ \ 4 \cdot F(3)$	(since 4 = 1 is false and hence $F(4)=4 \cdot F(3)$. This requires us to next compute $F(3)$, a recursive call on the function F)
	$= \ 4 \cdot 3 \cdot F(2)$	(since in computing $F(3)$ we find that 3=1 is false and hence $F(3)=3 \cdot F(2)$)
	$= \ 4 \cdot 3 \cdot 2 \cdot F(1)$	(since 2=1 is false and hence $F(2)=2 \cdot F(1)$)
	$= \ 4 \cdot 3 \cdot 2 \cdot 1$	(since 1=1 is true and hence the value of $F(1)$ is 1)
	$=24 = 4!$	

We will prove in Section 4.3 that for any positive integer X, $F(X) = X!$.

EXAMPLE 4.2.2
Consider the following recursive function that is applicable to any pair of nonnegative integers X1, X2.   This function is known as Ackermann's function.

$$A(X1,X2) \equiv IF \ \ X1=0 \ \ THEN \ X2+1$$

$$ELSE \ IF \ X2=0 \ THEN \ A(X1-1,1)$$

ELSE OTHERWISE A(X1-1,A(X1,X2-1))

Again let us trace the execution of this program for some particular values of X1 and X2.   For example,

A(1,2) = A(0,A(1,1))   (since X1=0 is false and X2=0 is false.   We must next compute A(1,1), a recursive call on A)

    = A(0,A(0,A(1,0)))   (since X1=0 is false and X2=0 is false.   We must next compute A(1,0)

    = A(0,A(0,A(0,1)))   (since X1=0 is false but X2=0 is true)

    = A(0,A(0,2))   (since X1=0 is true and hence A(0,1)=1+1=2)

    = A(0,3)   (since X1=0 is true and hence A(0,2)=2+1=3)

    = 4   (since X1=0 is true and hence A(0,3)=3+1=4)

The above example illustrates the fact that the computation sequence of a recursive program may be ambiguous and needs to be made more explicit.   For example, in computing A(0,A(1,1)) above, we assumed that A(1,1) should be computed before continuing with the computation of the outer call on A.   If we had chosen to carry out the computation of the outer call on A first, then the computation sequence would have been changed to be

A(1,2) = A(0,A(1,1))

    = A(1,1)+1

    = A(0,A(1,0))+1

    = (A(1,0)+1)+1

$$= (A(0,1)+1)+1$$

$$= (2+1)+1=4$$

The value computed for $A(1,2)$ is the same either way but the computation sequence is different. One can prove that if two different computation sequences are applied to the computation of the same recursive function with the same arguments and both computation sequences terminate, then the result will be the same. However, it is possible that one computation sequence will fail to terminate while a different computation sequence will terminate. We illustrate this in the next example.

EXAMPLE 4.2.3
Consider the following recursive program that is applicable to any pair of nonnegative integers X1, X2.

$F(X1,X2) \equiv$ IF X1 = 0 THEN 0

ELSE   OTHERWISE $F(0,F(X1,X2))$

Let us consider the computation of $F(1,1)$ using two different computation rules. In the first computation (i), we will always try to compute the outermost call of F first. In the second computation (ii), we will always try to compute the innermost call of F first.

(i) $F(1,1)$ = $F(0,F(1,1))$ (since   X1=0   is false)

= 0   (since   X1=0   is true   for   the outermost occurrence of F)

(ii) $F(1,1)$ = $F(0,F(1,1))$ (since   X1=0   is false)

= $F(0,F(0,F(1,1)))$ (since   X1=0   is false   for   the innermost occurrence of F)

= $F(0,F(0,F(0,F(1,1))))$

$$= F(0,F(0,F(0,F(O,F(1,1)))))) \text{ etc.}$$

Thus, using the first computation rule, the computation sequence for $F(1,1)$ terminates and $F(1,1)=0$. However, for the second computation rule, the computation sequence fails to terminate and hence $F(1,1)$ is undefined. Nevertheless, note that for any values of the arguments for which both computation sequences terminate, the result will be the same. For example, $F(0,M)=0$ regardless of which computation rule is used.

Thus we see that in order to make our programming language precise, we must specify what computation rule is to be applied to our programs to generate the computation sequence. We assume throughout this chapter that the computation rule to be applied to our programs is the <u>leftmost</u>, <u>innermost</u> rule. In other words, at each point in the computation sequence, the <u>leftmost</u>, <u>innermost</u> occurence of the function F (that is, the leftmost occurence of F that has all its arguments free of F's) is computed first. This compuation rule is not necessarily the best one, since it sometimes leads to a nonterminating computation sequence when a different rule would lead to a terminating sequence (as shown in Example 4.2.3). However, it is similar to the computation rule used in many actual programming languages. Also, as pointed out above for those computations that do terminate by this rule, the result is the same as for any other computation rule that terminates. Most of the programs we consider here terminate for all values of their arguments regardless of what computation rule is used, and hence the result of such computations will be the same regardless of what computation rule is applied. Nevertheless, to be specific, we assume that the leftmost, innermost computation rule is followed to generate the computation sequence.

Many of the example programs in this chapter deal with lists. We are using LISP like notation in such programs. A list is a collection of objects separated by blank spaces and enclosed between square brackets, [ ]. The objects that can occur in such lists are atoms and other lists. Atoms are strings of alphanumeric characters (without embedded blanks). We use the convention that such atoms must begin with one of the alphabetic characters A, B, C, D, or E, and that variables must begin with some letter other than A, B, C, D, or E. This allows us to distinguish between atoms and the variables used in defining our programs and allows us to avoid the more general QUOTE convention used in LISP. For example, [A B C] is a list of three elements, each of which is an atom.   [A[B A [C]] D C] is a list with four (top-level) elements.   The second of these four elements is itself a list, namely the list [B A [C]].   The third element of this list is also a list, namely [C].   We give the empty list (that is, the list that does not contain any elements) the special name NIL.   We also use the following tests and functions.

(i)   The test = can be applied to lists and atoms as well as numbers.   For example, [A B] = [A B] is true, [A B] = [B A] is false, [A B] = [A [B]] is false, B = A is false, and A = NIL is false.

(ii)   The test ATOM(X) can be applied to any object, that is, atoms or lists.   ATOM(X) results in the value TRUE if X is an atom or the empty list and results in the value FALSE if X is a nonempty list.

(iii)   The function CAR(L) can be applied to any nonempty list and results in the first (top-level) element of the list.   For example,

CAR([A B C]) is A

CAR([[A B]C]) is [A B]

CAR(NIL) is undefined

CAR(A) is undefined

(iv)   The function CDR(L) can be applied to any nonempty list and results in the list that is obtained from L by deleting its first (top-level) element.   For example,

CDR([A B C]) is [B C]

CDR ([[A B]C]) is [C]

CDR([B]) is NIL (or [ ])

CDR(NIL) is undefined

CDR(A) is undefined

(v) The function CONS(X,L) can be applied to any X (whether an atom or a list) and any list L. It results in a list that is like the list L but has X as its first element. For example,

CONS(A,[B C]) is [A B C]

CONS([A B], [B [C]]) is [[A B] B [C]]

CONS(A, NIL) is [A]

CONS(A, B) is undefined

We also use the special atoms TRUE and FALSE in defining some of our programs.

EXAMPLE 4.2.4

To illustrate these notations, let us write a recursive program that determines whether X is a (top-level) element of the list L.

MEMBER(X, L) ≡ IF L = NIL THEN FALSE

ELSE IF X=CAR(L) THEN TRUE

ELSE OTHERWISE MEMBER(X, CDR(L))

Let us trace the computation of this program for the actual arguments C, [A B C D].

MEMBER(C,[A B C D]) = MEMBER(C,[B C D])

= MEMBER(C,[C D])

= TRUE

Next let us trace the computation for the actual arguments C,[A B [C D]].

MEMBER(C,[A B [C D]]) = MEMBER(C,[B [C D]])

= MEMBER(C,[[C D]])

= MEMBER(C, NIL)

= FALSE

EXAMPLE 4.2.5

Let us write a recursive program that appends list L1 to

list L2, that is, forms a single list from the two lists by putting the elements of L1 before those of L2.

APPEND(L1, L2) ≡ IF L1 = NIL THEN L2

ELSE   OTHERWISE   CONS(CAR(L1),APPEND(CDR(L1),L2))

We now trace the computation of this program for several values of the arguments.

APPEND([A B],[C D]) = CONS(CAR([A B]),APPEND(CDR([A B]),

[C D])))

= CONS(A,APPEND([B],[C D])))

= CONS(A,CONS(CAR([B]),APPEND(CDR([B]),[C D])))

= CONS(A,CONS(B,APPEND(NIL,[C D])))

= CONS(A,CONS(B,[C,D])))

= CONS(A,[B C D])

= [A B C D]

APPEND([[A]],[B C]) = CONS([A],APPEND(NIL,[B C])

= CONS([A], [B C])

= [[A] B C]

APPEND([A B],NIL)   = CONS(A,APPEND([B],NIL))

= CONS(A,CONS(B,APPEND(NIL,NIL)))

= CONS(A,CONS(B,NIL))

= CONS(A,   [B])

= [A B]

EXERCISES

1.   Show the computation sequence when the program for Ackermann's function given in Example 4.2.2 is applied to compute
(a)   A(1,1)
(b)   A(2,1)
Use the leftmost, innermost computation rule in carrying out these computations.

2.   For the two computations in Exercise 1, show that the same values would be computed if, instead of

the leftmost, innermost computation rule, we use a rule that always evaluates the leftmost, outermost occurence of A first. For example, the computation (b) would then begin as

$$A(2,1) = A(1,A(2,0))$$
$$= A(0,A(1,A(2,0)-1))$$
$$= A(1,A(2,0)-1)+1$$

etc.

Note that in testing whether or not X2=0 for the last term of the computation sequence given above, we would be testing whether or not A(2,0)-1=0. This test should also be carried out by evaluating A(2,0) by the leftmost, outermost computation rule. However, to simplify the work done by students in generating this computation sequence, they may use the fact that

A(2,0)-1=0 is FALSE

A(2,0)-2=0 is FALSE

A(2,0)-3=0 is TRUE

when evaluated by the leftmost, outermost computation rule.

3. Consider the following recursive program that is applicable to any pair of integers X1, X2.

F(X1,X2) ≡ IF X2=0 THEN 0

ELSE OTHERWISE F(F(X1,X2-X1),X2-1)

Compute F(1,1) and F(0,1) using the leftmost, innermost and leftmost, outermost computation rules. Note that if the computation terminates using the leftmost, innermost rule, then it also terminates and gives the same value using the leftmost, outermost rule. However, it may fail to terminate using the leftmost, innermost rule when it does terminate using the leftmost, outermost rule. For the rest of the exercises and throughout the rest of this chapter, it is understood that we will always be using the leftmost, innermost computation rule.

4. Using the program given in Example 4.2.5, write out the computation sequence for

    (a)   APPEND(NIL,[A B C])

    (b)   APPEND([A B C],NIL)

    (c)   APPEND([A B]C], [D])

5. F(X,Y) ≡ IF X = 0 AND Y = 0 THEN 0

    ELSE IF X = 0 AND Y ≠ 0 THEN Y-1

    ELSE IF X ≠ 0 AND Y = 0 THEN X-1

    ELSE OTHERWISE F(F(X-1,Y),F(X,Y-1))

    Write out the computation sequence for

    (a)   F(1,1)

    (b)   F(2,1)

6. Consider the following recursive program that is applicable to any two lists L1,L2.

    INT(L1,L2) ≡ IF L1 = NIL THEN NIL

    ELSE IF MEMBER(CAR(L1),L2) THEN

    CONS(CAR(L1),INT(CDR(L1),L2))

    ELSE OTHERWISE INT(CDR(L1),L2)

    Write out the computation sequence for

    (a)   INT(NIL,[A B C])

    (b)   INT([B D C],[A B C])

    (c)   INT([[B D] C],[A B D])

    Note that this program uses the program MEMBER defined in Example 4.2.4.   In writing out the computation sequence for INT, do not bother to write out intermediate steps in the computation of MEMBER.   Assume MEMBER(X,L) gives value TRUE if X is a (top-level) element of the list L and FALSE otherwise.

4.3   STRUCTURAL INDUCTION

Recursive programs normally have the following basic form. They state directly how to compute the answer for the simplest value(s) of the data (arguments of the recursive function), and they next state how to compute the answer for more complicated data (arguments of the function) in terms of computations involving simpler data (arguments of the function when the function is called recursively). Thus it is natural to try to prove the correctness of such program by:

(i)   Proving that the program works correctly for the simplest value(s) of the data (arguments of the function).

(ii)   Proving that the program works correctly for more complicated data (arguments of the function) on the assumption that it works correctly fo simpler data (arguments of the function).

Such correctness proofs are natural for recursive programs because they follow the basic form of computation used by recursive programs. The reader, of course, should recognize (i) and (ii) as essentially being the two steps of an induction proof where the induction is upon the structure of the data manipulated by the program. In particular, if we can identify the intuitive notion of one data value (permissible argument of the function) being simpler than another with some well-ordering relation on the set of data values (permissible arguments of the function), then (i) and (ii) are exactly the two setps required in a (generalized) induction proof that the program works correctly for all permissible data values (arguments of the function). Correctness proofs that use this basic method of proof are said to be proofs by structural induction. We now illustrate the method by proving the correctness of several very simple recursive programs.

EXAMPLE   4.3.1

Let us prove the correctness of the recursive program given in Example 4.2.1:

$$F(X) \equiv \text{IF } X=1 \text{ THEN } 1$$

$$\text{ELSE OTHERWISE } X \cdot F(X-1)$$

This program is supposed to compute the factorial function.   Thus we wish to prove that for all positive
integers N, $F(N)=1\cdot2\cdots N=N!$ (N factorial).   The proof
is by structural induction using simple induction on the
positive integers.   Thus we need to:

    (i)   Prove that $F(1)=1!$.   But it is trivial to verify
          that $F(1)=1=1!$.

   (ii)   Prove (for all positive integers N) that if
          $F(N)=1\cdot2\cdots N=N!$ then $F(N+1)=1\cdot2\cdots N\cdot(N+1)=$
          $(N+1)!$.   So suppose that N is a positive
          integer and $F(N)=N!$ (the induction hypothe-
          sis).   Since N is a positive integer, the test
          $N+1=1$ is false and, thus, tracing the execution
          sequence of the program, we see that

$$F(N+1)=(N+1)\cdot F((N+1)-1)$$

$$=(N+1)\cdot F(N)$$

$$=(N+1)\cdot(N!) \text{ (by the induction hypothesis)}$$

$$=(N+1)\cdot(1\cdot2\cdots N)$$

$$=1\cdot2\cdots N\cdot(N+1)$$

$$=(N+1)!$$

This completes the proof by structural induction that for
all positive integers N, $F(N)=N!$.

EXAMPLE 4.3.2

Let us prove the correctness of the recursive program
given in Example 4.2.4:

    MEMBER(X,L) ≡ IF L=NIL THEN FALSE

                  ELSE IF X=CAR(L) THEN TRUE

                  ELSE OTHERWISE MEMBER(X,CDR(L))

This program is applicable to any element X and any list
L and is supposed to give the value TRUE if X is a
(top-level) element of the list L and FALSE otherwise,
that is,

           MEMBER(X,L)= TRUE if X is a (top-level)
                         element of L
                         FALSE Otherwise

We will prove that MEMBER works correctly by structural
induction.   Examination of the program shows that when
MEMBER is called recursively (line 3 of the program),
only the second of its two arguments is simpler than
before.   Thus it is natural for the induction to only be
on the structure of the second argument of the function.
When MEMBER is called recursively, its second argument
is CDR(L), which is a list that contains one less (top-
level) element than the list L.   Hence it is natural for
the structural induction to use simple induction on the
number of (top-level) elements in the list L.   Since this
number is always a nonnegative integer, the proof will
use simple induction on the nonnegative integers.   Thus
we need to:

(i)   Prove that for any list containing 0 elements,
MEMBER works correctly.   The only list with 0
elements is the empty list NIL.   MEMBER
(X,NIL)=FALSE, which is correct, since X is
not a (top-level) element of the list NIL.

(ii)   Prove (for all nonnegative integers N) that if
MEMBER works correctly for all lists L' that
contain N (top-level) elements, then MEMBER
also works correctly for all lists L that contain
N+1 (top-level) elements.   Therefore suppose
MEMBER does work correctly for lists L' of
length N, that is

```
MEMBER(X,L')= TRUE if X is a (top-level)
                 element of L'
             FALSE otherwise
```

(the induction hypothesis).   Suppose L is a
list that contains N+1 (top-level) elements.
Since N+1≥1 we know that L ≠ NIL.   Hence,
tracing the execution of the function, we see
that

```
MEMBER(X,L) =  TRUE if X=CAR(L)
               MEMBER(X,CDR(L)) otherwise
```

If X=CAR(L) [we know that CAR(L) is defined
because L ≠ NIL] then X is a (top-level)
element of the list L and hence the value
TRUE is the correct value.   If X ≠ CAR(L)

then X is a (top-level) element of the list L if and only if it is a (top-level) element of the list CDR(L) [we know that CDR(L) is defined because L ≠ NIL]. But CDR(L) is a list that contains N (top-level) elements. thus by the induction hypothesis we know that MEMBER (X,CDR(L)) correctly computes either TRUE or FALSE depending on whether X is a (top-level) element of CDR(L) or not. Thus, in the case where X ≠ CAR(L), MEMBER(X,L)= MEMBER(X,CDR(L)), which does compute the correct answer of either TRUE or FALSE depending on whether X is a (top-level) element of CDR(L) and hence of L or not.

This completes the proof by structural induction.

EXAMPLE 4.3.3

Let us prove the correctness of the recursive program given in Example 4.2.5:

```
APPEND(L1,L2) ≡ IF L1=NIL THEN L2

            ELSE OTHERWISE CONS(CAR(L1),APPEND(

                CDR(L1),L2))
```

This program is applicable to any two lists L1 and L2 and is supposed to result in a list made up of the elements of list L1 followed by those of L2. Examination of the program shows that when APPEND is called recursively, only the first of its two arguments is simpler than before. Thus the proof will be by structural induction using simple induction on the length (number of top-level elements) of the list L1. To carry out the correctness proof, we need to:

    (i)   Prove that for any list L1 of length 0, APPEND works correctly. The only list of length 0 is the empty list NIL. APPEND(NIL, L2)=L2, which is correct, since it is the list made up of the elements of L1 (there are no elements in L1) followed by those of L2.

   (ii) Prove (for all nonnegative integers N) that if APPEND works correctly for all lists L1' of length N, then APPEND also works correctly for all lists L1 of length N+1. So suppose that

APPEND does work correctly for all lists L1' of length N, that is, APPEND(L1',L2)= the list made up of the elements of L1' followed by those of L2 (the induction hypothesis). Suppose L1 is a list of length N+1. Since N+1 $\geqq$ 1, we know that L1 $\neq$ NIL. Hence tracing the execution of the function we see that APPEND (L1,L2)=CONS(CAR(L1),APPEND(CDR(L1),L2)) [we know that CAR(L1) and CDR(L1) are defined because L1 $\neq$ NIL]. But CDR(L1) is a list of length N. Thus by the induction hypothesis we know that APPEND(CDR(L1),L2)= the list made up of the elements of CDR(L1) followed by those of L2. Thus APPEND(CDR (L1),L2) = the list made up of all the elements of L1 except the first element of L1 followed by those of L2. But since CONS(CAR(L1), APPEND(CDR(L1),l2) forms a list that has the element CAR(L1) as its first element, followed by the elements of APPEND(CDR(L1),L2), we see that this is the list made up of all the elements of L1 (including the first element of L1,CAR(L1)) followed by those of L2. Thus APPEND works correctly in this case also. This completes the proof by structural induction.

MATHEMATICAL NOTE

We stated in the discussion at the beginning of this section that if the intuitive notion of one data value (permissible argument of the function) being simpler than another could be identified with some well-ordering relation < on the set of data values, then the correctness proof for a recursive program could be done by (generalized) induction on these data values. Notice that this is exactly what was done in Example 4.3.1, since the data values for that function are positive integers and the normal < relation well orders these data values. However, in Examples 4.3.2 and 4.3.3, we did not really have a well-ordering relation < defined on the data values(which were lists) for these programs. Instead we used a well-ordering on some property of the data values, namely the length of the list. The length of any list is a nonnegative integer, and the usual <

relation well orders the nonnegative integer. If we want to have a well-ordering relation < defined on the data values themselves (which are lists in this case) rather than on some property of the data values, we could have defined < by L1<L2 if and only if the length of L1 < the length of L2. This unfortunately does not quite define a well-ordering because the ordering < is only a partial ordering rather than a total ordering. For example, if L1 = [A B C] and L2 = [D E F] then we cannot say that L1<L2 or L2<L2 or L1=L2. In other words, some data values (those lists of the same length) are not comparable to one another, and thus the ordering defined by < is not total. This particular ordering < is thus not a well-ordering but it is what is sometimes called a well-founded ordering. It turns out that well-founded orderings (which are more general than well-orderings) are sufficient for doing induction proofs. Thus we could have done the proofs in Examples 4.3.2 and 4.3.3 by (generalized) induction on the data values ordered by the well-founded ordering <. The above well-founded ordering < could also be extended to a well-ordering <' by taking all lists of equal length to be equal in the ordering (rather than incomparable), but this is somewhat awkward. We will instead continue to do the induction proofs in this chapter by induction on some property of the data values (such as length) that is well ordered rather than worrying about formally defining either a well-founded ordering or well-ordering on the data values.

EXERCISES

1.   Consider the following recursive program that is applicable to any nonnegative integer N.

$$F(N) \equiv \text{IF } N = 0 \text{ THEN } 0$$
$$\text{ELSE OTHERWISE } F(F(N-1))$$

Prove that for all nonnegative integers N, $F(N) = 0$.

2.   Consider the following recursive program that is applicable to any positive integer N.

$$F(N) \equiv \text{IF } N = 1 \text{ THEN } 1$$

ELSE OTHERWISE F(N-1)+N

Prove that for all positive integers N, F(N) = (N·(N+1))/2.

3. Consider the following recursive program that is applicable to any nonnegative integer N.

F(N) ≡ IF N = 0 THEN 1

ELSE OTHERWISE 2·F(N-1)

Figure out a formula for the function computed by F(N) and prove it.

4. Consider the following recursive program that is applicable to any nonnegative integer N.

F(N) ≡ IF N ≤ 1 THEN N

ELSE OTHERWISE F (N-2)

Prove that for every even nonnegative integer, the value of F is 0, that is, for all nonnegative integers N, F(2·N) = 0. Also prove that for every odd nonnegative integer, the value of F is 1.

5. Consider the following recursive program that is applicable to any list L.

REVERSE (L) ≡ IF L = NIL THEN NIL

ELSE OTHERWISE APPEND(REVERSE

(CDR(L)),CONS(CAR(L),NIL))

Prove that for any list L, REVERSE(L) is the list that contains the same (top-level) elements as L but in the reverse order. In doing the proof you may assume that APPEND works correctly as shown in Example 4.3.3.

6. (a) Consider the following recursive program that is applicable to any object X and any list L.

DELETE1 (X,L) ≡ IF L=NIL THEN NIL

ELSE IF X=CAR(L) THEN CDR(L)

ELSE OTHERWISE CONS(CAR(L),

DELETE1(X,CDR(L)))

Prove that for any list L, DELETE1(X,L)= the list obtained from L by deleting the first top-level occurrence (if any) of X from L.   For example, DELETE1(B,[A[B] B C B]) = [A [B] C B].

(b)   Define a recursive program DELETE(X,L) that deletes all top level occurences of X from L.   Prove that your program works correctly.

7.   The following two functions are applicable to any two (lists that represent) sets.   A set is a list without repetitions, that is, such that no two top-level elements are the same.

```
INT(L1,L2) ≡ IF L1=NIL THEN NIL

              ELSE IF MEMBER(CAR(L1),L2) THEN

                 CONS(CAR(L1),INT(CDR(L1),L2))

              ELSE OTHERWISE INT(CDR(L1),L2)

UNION(L1,L2) ≡ IF L1=NIL THEN L2

              ELSE IF MEMBER(CAR(L1),L2) THEN

                 UNION (CDR(L1),L2)

              ELSE OTHERWISE CONS(CAR(L1),UNION

                        (CDR(L1),L2))
```

Prove that for any two sets L1, L2, INT(L1,L2) is the set intersection of L1 and L2, and union (L1,L2) is the set union of L1 and L2.   In other words,

INT(L1,L2)   = a set (list without repetitions) that contains all the elements that are in both L1 and L2.

UNION(L1,L2)=a set (list without repetitions) that contains all the elements that are in either L1 or L2 or both

You may assume that MEMBER works correctly as shown in Example 4.3.2.

8.   Consider the following recursive program that is applicable to any two sets L1,L2.

```
F(L1,L2) ≡ IF L1=NIL THEN TRUE
```

```
        ELSE IF MEMBER(CAR(L1),L2) THEN

                          F(CDR(L1),L2)

        ELSE OTHERWISE FALSE
```

Discover what the above function does and then prove it.

9. Consider the following two recursive programs. LEAST is applicable to any nonempty list of numbers, L1. SORT is applicable to any list of numbers, L2.

```
LEAST(L1) ≡ IF CDR(L1)=NIL THEN CAR(L1)

            ELSE IF CAR(L1) ≦ LEAST(CDR(L1)) THEN

                                      CAR(L1)

            ELSE OTHERWISE LEAST (CDR(L1))

SORT(L2) ≡ IF L2=NIL THEN L2

            ELSE OTHERWISE CONS(LEAST(L2),SORT

                (DELETE1 (LEAST(L2),L2)))
```

Prove that for any nonempty list of numbers L2, SORT(L2) is the list L2 sorted into nondescending order. In order to do this proof, first prove that for any nonempty list of numbers L1, LEAST(L1) is the least number in the list L1. You may assume that DELETE 1 works as shown in Exercise 6.

10. Here we wish to investigate how errors in programs cause the attempted correctness proofs to break down. For each of the following erroneous programs attempt to prove the correctness of the program as before, and see where the attempted proof fails. After finding an error in the attempted proof, find specific values of the data for which the program computes the wrong answer.

(a) Suppose the program in Exercise 2 had mistakenly been:

```
(i)  F(N) ≡ IF N=1 THEN 2

            ELSE OTHERWISE F(N-1)

(ii) F(N) ≡ IF N=1 THEN 1

            ELSE OTHERWISE F(N-1)+1
```

      (iii)F(N) ≡ IF N=1 THEN 1

                  ELSE OTHERWISE F(N-1)+N-1

(b) Suppose the program of Exercise 6a had mistakenly been:

DELETE1(X,L) ≡ IF L=NIL THEN NIL

              ELSE IF X=CAR(L) THEN CDR(L)

              ELSE OTHERWISE DELETE1(X,

                                        CDR(L))

(c) Suppose the programs in Exercise 7 had mistakenly been:

(i)   INT(L1,L2) ≡ IF L1=NIL THEN NIL

              ELSE OTHERWISE INT(CDR(L1),L2)

(ii) INT(L1,L2) ≡ IF L1=NIL THEN NIL

              ELSE IF MEMBER(CAR(L1),L2) THEN

                    CONS(CAR(L1),INT(CDR(L1),

                            CDR(L2)))

              ELSE OTHERWISE INT(CDR(L1),L2)

(iii)INT(L1,L2) ≡ IF L1=NIL THEN NIL

              ELSE IF MEMBER(CAR(L1),L2) THEN

                    CONS(CAR(L1),INT(CDR(L1),L2))

              ELSE OTHERWISE INT(L1,L2)

(iv) UNION(L1,L2) ≡ IF L1=NIL THEN NIL

              ELSE IF MEMBER(CAR(L1),L2) THEN

                    UNION(CDR(L1),L2)

              ELSE OTHERWISE CONS(CAR(L1),

                    UNION(CAR(L1),L2))

4.4 MORE DIFFICULT EXAMPLES OF STRUCTURAL INDUCTION

The structural induction proofs in this section use

either the stronger version of induction (Section 1.3) or generalized induction (Section 1.4). The reader who skipped one or both of these sections should now return to the study them before continuing with this section.

EXAMPLE   4.4.1

Consider the following recursive program that is applicable to any object X and list L.

```
MEMBER1(X,L) ≡ IF X=NIL THEN FALSE
                 ELSE IF X=CAR(L) THEN TRUE
                 ELSE IF ATOM(CAR(L))THEN MEMBER1(X,
                                               CDR(L))
                 ELSE IF MEMBER1(X,CAR(L))THEN TRUE
                 ELSE OTHERWISE MEMBER1(X,CDR(L))
```

We wish to prove that

MEMBER1(X,L) = TRUE IF X occurs as an element (at any level) in list L
FALSE otherwise

The proof will be by strong induction on the total number, n, of occurrence of parentheses and atoms in the list L. For example, the list [[A B] C [[B [A]]] has n = 14 occurrences of parentheses and atoms while the CAR(L) has n=4 occurrences of parentheses and atoms. The smallest possible possible total number of occurrences of parentheses and atoms that a list can have is for the empty list NIL=[ ], which has n=2. To carry out the correctness proof, we need to:

(i)   Prove that if L is such that n=2, then MEMBER1 works correctly. But if n=2 then L must be the empty list NIL and hence

MEMBER1(X,L) = MEMBER(X,NIL)

= FALSE

This is correct, since X does not occur at any level in the empty list.

(ii) Prove (for all n ≥ 2) that if MEMBER1(X,L') works correctly for any list L' with n'<n+1 total number of occurrences of parentheses and

atoms, then MEMBER1(X,L) also works correctly for any list L with n+1 total occurrences of parentheses and atoms (i.e., we are using strong induction on n).   So suppose MEMBER1 (X,L') does work correctly for any such list L' with n'<n+1 (the induction hypothesis), and suppose L is any list with n+1 total number of occurrences of parentheses and atoms.   We know that L≠NIL.   If X=CAR(L), then the value of MEMBER1(X,L) is TRUE, which is correct, since X does then occur as an element of L.   If X≠CAR(L) and ATOM(CAR(L))=TRUE, then MEMBER1(X,L)=MEMBER1(X,CDR(L)). But CDR(L) is a list that contains n'<n+1 total number of occurrences of parentheses and atoms.   Thus the induction hypothesis assures us that MEMBER1(X,CDR(L)) correctly computes to either TRUE or FALSE depending on whether X occurs as an element (at any level) in CDR(L) or not.   But since X≠CAR(L) and ATOM(CAR(L))=TRUE, we know the X occurs as an element in L if and only if X occurs as an element in CDR(L).   Thus this is also the correct value for whether or not X occurs as an element in L.   If X≠CAR(L) and ATOM(CAR (L))=FALSE AND MEMBER1(X,CAR(L))=TRUE then the value of MEMBER1(X,L) is TRUE. This is correct, for we know that in this case CAR(L) is a list, and CAR(L) contains n'<n+1 total number of occurrences of parentheses and atoms.   Thus the induction hypothesis assures us that MEMBER1(X,CAR(L)) works correctly and, hence, if MEMBER1(X,CAR(L))=TRUE, then X does occur as an element in CAR(L) and hence also in L.   Finally, if X≠CAR(L) and ATOM(CAR(L))=FALSE and MEMBER1(X, CAR(L))=FALSE then MEMBER1(X,L)=MEMBER1 (X,CDR(L)).   But CDR(L) is a list that contains n'<n+1 total number of occurrences of parentheses and atoms, and thus the induction hypothesis assures us that MEMBER1(X,CDR (L)) correctly computes either TRUE or FALSE depending on whether or not X occurs as an element in CDR(L).   But since, in this case,

we have X≠CAR(L) and ATOM(CAR(L))=FALSE and MEMBER1(X,CAR(L))=FALSE, then we know that X occurs as an element in L if and only if X occurs as an element in CDR(L), and hence the value computed for MEMBER1(X,L)= MEMBER1(X,CDR(L)) will again be correct in this case.

EXAMPLE   4.4.2

Consider Ackermann's function that was introduced in Example 4.2.2.

A(X1,X2) ≡ IF X1=0 THEN X2+1

        ELSE IF X2=0 THEN A(X1-1,1)

        ELSE OTHERWISE A(X1-1, A(X1,X2-1))

This program is applicable to any two nonnegative integers, X1,X2. Let us prove by structural induction that the computation of A terminates for all pairs of nonnegative integers. We observe that the first place where A is called recursively [the second line of the program, A(X1-1,1)], its first argument is smaller than before. The second place where A is called recursively [the third line of the program, A(X1-1, A(X1,X2-1))], the first argument of the outer call is smaller than before, while the second argument of the inner call is smaller than before. This suggests that the induction should be generalized induction on the set of ordered pairs <X1,X2> of nonnegative integers well ordered by the lexicographic ordering <. Recall from Example 1.4.3 and Exercise 1 at the end of Section 1.4 that < is defined by <X1',X2'> < <x1,X2> if and only if (X1'<X1) or (X1'=X1 and X2'<X2). Let us prove by generalized induction that the computation of A terminates for all pairs of nonnegative integers X1,X2. We need to:

   (i)   Prove that the computation of A(X1,X2) terminates for the smallest element in the well-ordered set. But <0,0> is the smallest element, and clearly the computation of A(0,0) terminates.

  (ii)   Prove (for all pairs of nonnegative integers <X1,X2> > <0,0>) that if the computation of A(X1',X2') terminates for all <X1',X2'> < X1,X

X2>, then the computation of A(X1,X2)also terminates. Therefore, suppose we have a pair of nonnegative integers <X1,X2> ><0,0>, and we know that the computation of A(X1', X2') terminates for all <X1',X2'> < <X1,X2> (the induction hypothesis). If X1=0 then it is clear that the computation of A(X1,X2) terminates. If X1≠0 but X2=0 then the computation sequence is A(X1,X2)=A(X1-1,1). But <X1-1,1> < <X1,X2> and, thus, by the induction hypothesis, the computation of A(X1-1,1) terminates and hence the computation of A(X1, X2) also terminates. If X1≠0 and X2≠0 then the computation sequence is A(X1,X2)=A(X1-1, A(X1,X2-1)). Using the leftmost, innermost computation rule, we know that the computation will next continue by evaluating A(X1, X2-1). But <X1, X2-1> < <X1,X2> and, thus, by the induction hypothesis, we know that the computation of A(X1,X2-1) will terminate. When it does the computation will next proceed to evaluate A(X1-1,Z) where Z is the value obtained for A(X1,X2-1). But regardless of the value of Z, <X1-1,Z> < <X1,X2>. Thus, by the induction hypothesis, we know that the computation of A(X1-1,Z) will terminate and hence the computation of A(X1,X2) will eventually terminate after computing A(X1,X2-1)=Z and A(X1-1,Z).

EXAMPLE 4.4.3

Consider the following recursive program that is applicable to any integer (positive, negative, or 0) N.

$$F(N) \equiv IF\ N > 100\ THEN\ N-10$$

$$ELSE\ OTHERWISE\ F(F(N+11))$$

We wish to prove that $F(N) = $ N-10 if N>100

91 otherwise, i.e., if N≤100

This function was given as an example by John McCarthy and is usually referred to as McCarthy's 91 function. We observe that when F is called recursively, its argument, N+11, is larger than before. The simplest cases correspond to any value of N > 100. Thus larger values of N correspond to simpler cases. For this reason let us define a well-ordering <' on the set {N : N is an integer and N ≤ 100} by N1 <' N2 if and only if N2 < N1 (where this is the usual < for integers). We use generalized induction on the above well-ordered set in the proof that

$$F(N) = \begin{array}{l} N\text{-}10 \text{ if } N{>}100 \\ 91 \text{ otherwise} \end{array}$$

It is immediately apparent that if N > 100 then F(N) = N-10. Thus in order to prove the above we only need to show that if N ≤ 100, then F(N) = 91. To do so by generalized induction, we need to:

(i)   Prove that F(N) = 91 for the smallest element in the set. In the ordering defined by <',100 is the smallest element. Thus we need to show that F(100)=91. The computation sequence for F(100) is

F(100) = F(F(100+11)) = F(F(111))

          = F(101)

          = 91

Hence it is true, that F(100)=91.

(ii)   Prove (for 100 <'N)(i.e., N < 100 for the usual < relation) that if F(N')=91 for all N'<'N (i.e., N<N'≤100), then F(N)=91. So suppose 100<'N and F(N')=91 for all N'<'N (the induction hypothesis). Then, since N<100, we would have F(N)=F(F(N+11)). If N+11 is in the set {N : N is an integer and N≤100}, then N+11<'N(i.e., N<N+11≤100), and we can apply the induction hypothesis to the above and have

F(N)=F(F(N+11))

      =F(91) (by the induction hypothesis)

If N+11 is in the set then N+11≤100 or N≤89. But then 91<'N (i.e., N<91) and thus we can apply the induction hypothesis again to get

```
F(N)=F(F(N+11))
```

$\quad$ =F(91) (by the induction hypothesis)

$\quad$ =91 (by the induction hypothesis again)

If N+11 is not in the set then of course we cannot apply the induction hypothesis to F(F(N+11)). However, if N+11 is not in the set, then we know that N+11>100. Thus we would have

```
F(N)=F(F(N+11))
```

$\quad$ =F((N+11)-10) (since N+11>100)

$\quad$ =F(N+1)

Now N+1 must be in the set because N<100 and thus N+1<100. Furthermore, N+1 <' N (i.e, N<N+1≦100), and hence we can apply the induction hypothesis to get

```
F(N)=F(F(N+11))
```

$\quad$ =F((N+11)-10)

$\quad$ =F(N+1)

$\quad$ =91 $\qquad$ (by the induction hypothesis)

This completes the proof by structural induction that if N≦100 then F(N)=91.

EXAMPLE   4.4.4

Consider the following recursive program that is applicable to any two lists of integers L1,L2, such that the integers occur in each list in ascending order.

```
INTORD(L1,L2) ≡ IF L1=NIL THEN NIL
                ELSE IF L2=NIL THEN NIL
                ELSE IF CAR(L1)<CAR(L2) THEN
                        INTORD(CDR(L1),L2)
                ELSE IF CAR(L2)<CAR(L1) THEN
                        INTORD(L1,CDR(L2))
```

```
                ELSE OTHERWISE CONS(CAR(L1),

                       INTORD(CDR(L1),CDR(L2)))
```

We wish to prove that for any two such ordered lists of integers L1,L2, INTORD(L1,L2) is the ordered list of all numbers that are elements of both L1 and L2, that is, INTORD(L1,L2) is the "intersection" of the ordered lists L1,L2. We observe that when INTORD is called recursively, either the first argument is simpler than before, or the second argument is simpler than before, or both arguments are simpler than before. Thus it is natural to do the proof by generalized induction on the pairs of possible lengths <LENGTH1,LENGTH2> of L1,L2 ordered lexicographically by <. Thus we need to:

(i)   Prove that for ordered lists of numbers L1, L2 with the smallest lengths, the function works correctly. But the smallest lengths are <0,0>, and thus L1 and L2 are the empty lists. INTORD(NIL,NIL)=NIL, which is correct.

(ii) Prove (for all pairs of lengths <LENGTH1, LENGTH2> > <0,0>) that if INTORD(L1',L2') is correct for all lists L1',L2' such that <LENGTH1',LENGTH2'> < <LENGTH1,LENGTH2>, then INTORD(L1,L2) is also correct (where L1 and L2 have lengths LENGTH1 and LENGTH2). So suppose we have L1 and L2 as above and the induction hypothesis is true. It is easy to check that if either L1 or L2 is NIL then INTORD(L1,L2)=NIL, which is correct. Therefore, suppose L1≠NIL and L2≠NIL. We must have one of three possibilities: either (a) CAR(L1)<CAR(L2), or (b) CAR(L2)<CAR(L1), or (c) CAR(L1)=CAR(L2). In case (a) INTORD (L1,L2)=INTORD(CDR(L1),L2). But the length of CDR(L1) is less than the length of L1, and hence <Length of CDR(L1), Length of L2> < <Length1, Length2> in the lexicographic ordering. Thus the induction hypothesis applies and tells us that INTORD(CDR(L1),L2) is the ordered list of all numbers that are elements of both CDR(L1) and L2. But since CAR(L1)<CAR(L2) and L1 and L2 are ordered, we know that CAR(L1) is not an element of

L2.   Hence the ordered list of all numbers that
are elements of both CDR(L1) and L2 is the
same as the ordered list of all numbers that
are elements of both L1 and L2.   Thus in this
case   INTORD(L1,L2)=INTORD(CDR(L1),L2)   is
correct.   In case (b) INTORD(L1,L2)=INTORD
(L1,CDR(L2)).   But the length of CDR(L2) is
less than the length of L2, and hence <length
of   L1,   length   of   CDR(L2)>   <   <LENGTH1,
LENGTH2>   in   the   lexicographic   ordering.
Thus   the   induction   hypothesis   applies   to
INTORD(L1,CDR(L2))   and,   by   an   argument
similar to that of case (a), leads to the conclusion that INTORD(L1,L2) is correct in this
case also.   In case (c) we have INTORD(L1,
L2)=CONS(CAR(L1),INTORD(CDR(L1),CDR(L2)
)).   But the lengths of CDR (L1) and CDR(L2)
are less than the lengths of L1 and L2, and
hence   the   induction   hypothesis   applies   to
INTORD(CDR(L1),CDR(L2)).   The   induction
hypothesis tells us that INTORD (CDR(L1),
CDR (L2)) is the ordered list of all numbers
that are elements of both CDR(L1) and CDR
(L2).   In this case we also have that CAR
(L1)=CAR(L2),   and   hence   CAR(L1)   [or   CAR
(L2)] should be an element of the correct list.
CONS(CAR(L1),   INTORD(CDR(L1),CDR (L2)))
is the ordered list of numbers that are elements of both CDR(L1) and CDR(L2), with the
one additional element CAR(L1) at the beginning of the list.   But this is the correct list,
and hence in this case also INTORD(L1, L2) is
correct.   This completes the proof for this
program.
    Review the four examples here and observe that we
really needed either the stronger version of induction or
generalized induction for each of these proofs.   Simple
induction would not have sufficed for any of them.   Also
notice that the lexicographic ordering is often useful in
dealing with recursive programs of two or more arguments when the program has recursive calls in which one
time one of the arguments is simpler and another time a
different one of the arguments is simpler (see Examples
4.4.2 and 4.4.4).

EXERCISES

1. Prove that for all nonnegative integers X1,X2, $A(X1,X2)>X1+X2$. $A(X1,X2)$ is Ackermann's function discussed in Example 4.4.2.

2. Consider the following recursive program that is applicable to any integer N.

$$F(N) \equiv \text{IF } N>202 \text{ THEN } N-3$$

$$\text{ELSE OTHERWISE } F(F(N+4))$$

Prove that for all integers N,

$$F(N) = \begin{cases} N-3 \text{ if } N>202 \\ 200 \text{ otherwise, i.e., if } N \leq 202 \end{cases}$$

3. Consider the following recursive program that is applicable to any nonnegative integer X.

$$F(X) \equiv \text{IF } X=0 \text{ THEN } 0$$

$$\text{ELSE IF EVEN}(X) \text{ THEN } F(X/5)+5$$

$$\text{ELSE OTHERWISE } F(3 \cdot X+1)-1$$

Even (X) is a test that gives value TRUE if X is an even integer and FALSE if X is an odd integer. $X/5$ is the integer quotient of the integer division of X by 5. Prove that the above program terminates for all nonnegative integers X.

4. Consider the following recursive program that is applicable to any integer N.

$$F(N) \equiv \text{IF } N>100 \text{ THEN } N-10$$

$$\text{ELSE OTHERWISE } F(F(F(N+21)))$$

Prove that for any integer N,

$$F(N) = \begin{cases} N-10 \text{ if } N>100 \\ 91 \text{ otherwise, i.e., if } N \leq 100 \end{cases}$$

5. Consider the following recursive program that is applicable to any two nonnegative integers X1,X2.

$$F(X1,X2) \equiv \text{IF } X1=0 \text{ THEN } 0$$

$$\text{ELSE IF } X2=0 \text{ THEN } F(X1-1,X2+1)$$

$$\text{ELSE OTHERWISE } F(F(X1-1,X2),F(X1,X2-1))$$

Discover what F(X1,X2) computes and prove it.
6.   Consider the following recursive program that is applicable to any two nonnegative integers X1,X2.

        F(X1,X2) ≡ IF X1=0 THEN X2

                        ELSE IF X2=0 THEN F(X1-1,X2+1)

                        ELSE OTHERWISE F(X1,X2-1)+1

Discover what F(X1,X2) computes and prove it.
7.   Consider the following recursive program that is applicable to any two nonnegative integers X1,X2

        F(X1,X2) ≡ IF X2=0 THEN X1

                        ELSE IF X1=0 THEN F(1,X2-1)

                        ELSE OTHERWISE F(F(X1-1,X2),X2-1)

Prove that for all nonnegative integers, X1, X2,
$$F(X1,X2) = \begin{cases} X1 \text{ if } X2=0 \\ 1 \text{ otherwise, i.e., if } X2 \neq 0 \end{cases}$$

8.   Consider the following recursive program that is applicable to any two integers X1,X2 such that 0≤X1≤X2 and 0<X2.

        F(X1,X2) ≡ IF X1=0 THEN X2

                        ELSE IF X1≤X2-X1 THEN F(X1,X2-X1)

                        ELSE OTHERWISE F(X2-X1,X1)

Prove that for any two integers X1,X2, such that 0≤X1≤X2 and 0<X2, F(X1,X2)=GCD(X1,X2) (the greatest common divisor of X1,X2). The proof will use the fact that for any such integers X1,X2, GCD(X1,X2)=GCD(X1,X2-X1)=GCD(X2-X1,X1).
9.   Consider the following recursive program that is applicable to any list L.

FLATTEN(L) ≡ IF L=NIL THEN NIL

                        ELSE IF ATOM(CAR(L))THEN CONS(

                        CAR(L),FLATTEN(CDR(L)))

                        ELSE OTHERWISE APPEND(FLATTEN(

                        CAR(L)),FLATTEN(CDR(L)))

Prove that for any list L, FLATTEN(L) is the list of all atoms that occur in L with all internal list structure deleted. For example, FLATTEN ([[A [B]]C [[D[A B]]]])=[A B C D A B].

10. Define a recursive program UNIONORD(L1,L2) similar to INTORD, defined in Example 4.4.4. UNIONORD(L1,L2) should be applicable to any two lists of integers L1,L2, such that the integers occur in each list in ascending order. It should result in the ordered list of all integers that are elements of either L1,L2 or both; that is, UNION-ORD(L1,L2) is the "union" of the ordered lists L1 and L2. Prove your program is correct.

11. Consider the following recursive program that is applicable to any two lists L1,L2.

```
DELETE2(L1,L2) ≡ IF L1=NIL THEN L2

                 ELSE IF L2=NIL THEN NIL

                 ELSE OTHERWISE DELETE2(CDR(L1),

                 DELETE(CAR(L1),L2))
```

This program uses the DELETE function you defined and proved correct in Exercise 6b of the preceeding section (Section 4.3). Prove that for any two lists L1, L2, DELETE2(L1,L2) is the list obtained from L2 by deleting from it all occurrences of (top-level) elements in L1.

12. Consider the following recursive program that is applicable to any two atoms X1,X2 and any list L.

```
SUBS(X1,X2,L) ≡ IF L=NIL THEN NIL

                ELSE IF CAR(L)=X2 THEN

                CONS(X1,SUBS(X1,X2,CDR(L)))

                ELSE IF ATOM(CAR(L)) THEN

                CONS(CAR(L),SUBS(X1,X2,CDR(L)))

                ELSE OTHERWISE CONS(SUBS(X1,X2,

                CAR(L)),SUBS(X1,X2,CDR(L)))
```

Prove that for any two atoms X1,X2 and any list L, SUBS(X1,X2,L) is the list obtained from L by substituting X1 for every occurence of X2 in L. For example, SUBS(B,C,[A B C[A[C]]]) is [A B B[A[B]]].

13. Here we wish to investigate how errors in programs cause the attempted correctness proofs to break down. For each of the following erroneous programs, attempt to prove the correctness of the program as before and see where the attempted proof fails. After finding an error in the attempted proof, find specific value(s) of the data for which the program computes the wrong answer.

(a) Suppose the program in Exercise 7 had mistakenly been

(i) F(X1,X2) ≡ IF X2=0 THEN X1

                        ELSE IF X1=0 THEN F(X1-1,1)

                        ELSE OTHERWISE F(F(X1-1,X2),X2-1)

(ii) F(X1,X2) ≡ IF X2=0 THEN 1

                        ELSE IF X1=0 THEN F(X2-1,1)

                        ELSE OTHERWISE F(F(X1-1,X2),X2-1)

(iii)F(X1,X2) ≡ IF X2=0 THEN X1

                        ELSE IF X1=0 THEN F(1,X2-1)

                        ELSE OTHERWISE F(F(X1-1,X2),X2)

(b) Suppose the program in Exercise 9 had mistakenly been

(i) FLATTEN(L) ≡ IF ATOM(CAR(L)) THEN CONS(

                        CAR(L),FLATTEN(CDR(L)))

                        ELSE OTHERWISE APPEND(FLATTEN(

                        CAR(L)),FLATTEN(CDR(L)))

(ii) FLATTEN(L) ≡ IF L=NIL THEN NIL

                        ELSE IF ATOM(CAR(L))THEN

                        CONS(CAR(L),FLATTEN(CDR(L)))

                        ELSE OTHERWISE CONS(FLATTEN

                        (CAR(L)),FLATTEN(CDR(L)))

(iii)FLATTEN(L) ≡ IF L=NIL THEN NIL

                           ELSE OTHERWISE CONS(CAR(L),

                                     FLATTEN(CDR(L)))

4.5 STRUCTURAL INDUCTION FOR NONRECURSIVE PROGRAMS

In Chapter 2 we introduced the method of inductive assertions for proving the correctness of nonrecursive (iterative) programs. However, in proving the correctness of nonrecursive programs that are essentially carrying out recursive processes, the method of structural induction is sometimes easier to use than the method of inductive assertions. In this section we illustrate several examples of this.

EXAMPLE 4.5.1

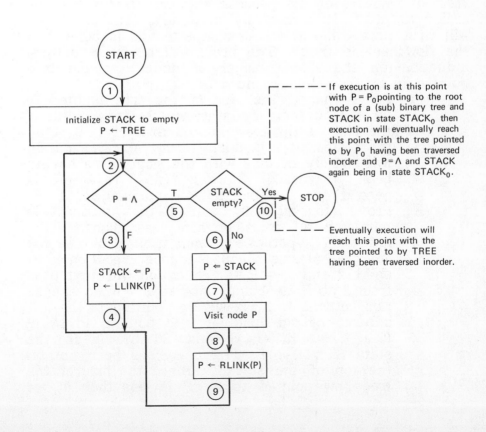

If execution is at this point with $P = P_0$ pointing to the root node of a (sub) binary tree and STACK in state $STACK_0$ then execution will eventually reach this point with the tree pointed to by P_0 having been traversed inorder and $P = \Lambda$ and STACK again being in state $STACK_0$.

Eventually execution will reach this point with the tree pointed to by TREE having been traversed inorder.

We wish to prove that if the above flowchart is executed with TREE being a pointer to the root node (TREE=Λ if the tree is the empty tree) of a binary tree, then execution will eventually terminate and when it does all nodes of the tree will have been visited inorder (see pages 315-318 of The Art of Computer Programming, Vol. 1, Second Edition, by D. E. Knuth for a discussion of tree traversal algorithms and the notation used in this flowchart).   Recall that inorder means that for each node of the tree, all of the nodes of the left subtree of that node are visited (inorder), and then the node is visited, and then all of the nodes of the right subtree of that node are visited (inorder).   This program is essentially carrying out a recursive process and could have been programmed more easily in a recursive manner.   In this nonrecursive version the algorithm makes use of an explicit stack.   We could prove this program correct by the method of inductive assertions (see Exercise 1 at the end of this section).   Nevertheless, the essentially recursive nature of the process suggests that it may be easier to prove it correct by structural induction.   We will first prove that the statement attached to point 2 in the flowchart is true.   The proof will be by structural induction on the size (number of nodes) of the tree pointed to by P.   Thus we need to:

(i)   Prove that if the size of the tree pointed to by P is 0 then the statement is true.   But if the size of the tree pointed to by P is 0, then the statement is trivially true, since execution will already be at 2 with the empty tree having been traversed inorder (no traversal is needed) and P=Λ and STACK unchanged.

(ii)   Prove (for all $n>0$) that if the statement is true for all trees of size less than n (the induction hypothesis), then it is also true for any tree of size n.   So suppose execution is at point 2 and $P = P_0 \neq \Lambda$, execution will next pass from 2 to 3 to 4 and back to 2.   When execution returns to 2, P will be pointing to the left subtree of the original tree pointed to by P (i.e., $P=LLINK(P_0)$] and STACK is in the state $STACK_0$, P_0 (i.e., P_0 has been put on the top of the stack).   Since the size of the tree now pointed to by P is less than n, we

know by the induction hypothesis that execution will eventually return to 2 with this left
subtree having been traversed inorder and $P=\Lambda$
and STACK again in the state $STACK_0$, P_0.
Next, since $P=\Lambda$, execution will proceed from 2
to 5 to 6 to 7 to 8 to 9 and back to 2. When
execution returns to 2 we have $P=RLINK(P_0$
and STACK in the state $STACK_0$, and the
original root node will have been visited.
Thus so far the nodes of the left subtree will
have been visited inorder and the root node
will have been visited. Now the pointer P will
be pointing to the right subtree and hence to
a smaller tree than the original tree pointed to
by P_0. Thus the induction hypothesis will
apply and tells us that execution will eventually return to this point with the tree
pointed to by P (the right subtree of the
original tree) having been traversed inorder
and $P=\Lambda$, and STACK in the state $STACK_0$.
At that point, the left subtree will have been
traversed inorder, the original root node
visited, and the right subtree traversed inorder. But this implies that the original tree
has been traversed inorder. We will also have
$P=\Lambda$ and STACK in the state $STACK_0$. This
completes the induction proof.

The above proof easily leads to the correctness
proof, since the first time execution reaches 2 (from 1),
we will have that P=TREE and STACK is empty. The
statement attached to 2 that we have just proved implies
that execution will eventually reach 2 with the tree
pointed to by P having been traversed inorder and $P=\Lambda$
and STACK in its original state, empty. At that point,
since $P=\Lambda$, execution will proceed to 5 and, since STACK
is empty, execution will next proceed to 10, which shows
that the correctness assertion attached to 10 is true.

EXAMPLE 4.5.2

We wish to prove the program on the following page
is correct. If the value, N_0, read in for N, is greater
than 100 then it is apparent that execution will follow
the path 1 to 2 to 3 to 8 to 9 to 10 and, consequently,

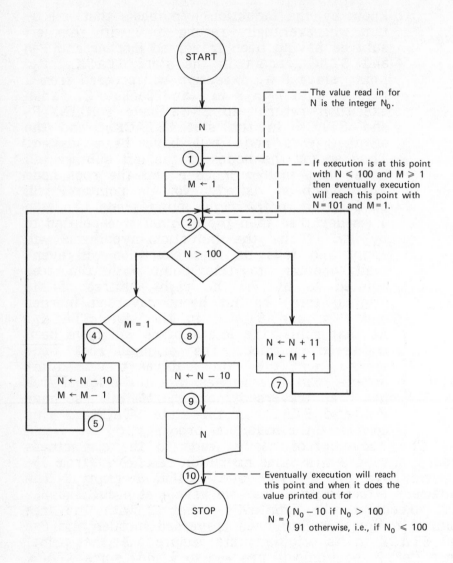

execution will eventually reach point 10, and the value printed out for N will be $N_0 - 10$. Thus we only need to prove that if the value N_0, read in for N, is less than or equal to 100 then execution will eventually reach point 10, and the value printed out for N will be 91. To prove this let us first prove by structural induction that the assertion attached to 2 is true. The proof will use generalized induction on the set, $X = \{<n,m> : n,m$

are integers and n $\leq$ 100 and m $\geq$ 1}, well ordered by
the realtion <n1, m1> < <n2,m2> if and only if (n1 > n2)
or (n1 = n2 and m1 < m2); that is, the well-ordering is
    <100,1> < <100,2> < <100,3> · · · < <100,n> · · ·
    < <99,1> < <99,2> < · · · ·

    < <98,1> < <99,2> < · · · ·etc.

The student should verify that this is indeed a well-
ordering.   In order to carry out this generalized induction proof, we need to:

(i)   Prove that the assertion is true for $N=n_0$ and
      $M=m_0$ where $<n_0,m_0>$ is the smallest element in
      the above set.   The smallest element in the
      above set is <100,1>, and thus we need to
      prove that if execution is at point 2 with
      N=100 and M=1, then eventually execution will
      reach point 2 with N=101 and M=1.   So suppose
      execution is at point 2 and N=100 and M=1.
      The test N > 100 would be false, and hence
      execution would next proceed from 2 to 6 to 7
      and back to 2.   When execution returns to 2
      we would have n=100+11=111 and M=1+1=2.   The
      test N > 100 would be true, and therefore
      execution would next proceed from 2 to 3.
      Since the test M=1 would be false, execution
      would next proceed from 3 to 4 to 5 and back
      to 2.   When execution returned to 2 we would
      have N=111-10=101 and M=2-1=1.   But this is
      what we need to prove, that is, that even-
      tually execution would return to point 2 with
      N=101 and M=1.

(ii) Prove (for all <n,m> > <100,1>) that if the
      assertion is true for N = n' and M=m' for all
      <n', m'> < <n,m> (the induction hypothesis),
      then the assertion is also true for N=n and
      M=m.   So suppose execution is at point 2 and
      N=n and M=m, and the induction hypothesis is
      true.   The test N > 100 would be false, and
      hence execution would next proceed from 2 to
      6 to 7 and back to 2.   When execution returns
      to 2 N=n+11 and M=m+1.   If n+11 $\leq$ 100 then
      <n+11, m+1> is in the set X.   In that case
      <n+11, m+1> < <n,m>, and thus we could apply
      the induction hypothesis to conclude that even-

tually execution will reach 2 with N=101 and
M=1. So we only need to consider further the
case where n+11>100, that is, the case where n
> 89. In this case execution would be at 2
with N=n+11 > 100 and M=m+1. The test n >
100 would be true and the test M=1 would be
false, and hence execution would next proceed
from 2 to 3 to 4 to 5 and back to 2. When
execution returns to 2 we will have N=(n+11)-
10=n+1 and M=(m+1)-1=m. If n+1≤100 then
<n+1,m> is in the set X. In that case <n+1,
m> < <n,m>, and thus we could again apply the
induction hypothesis to obtain the conclusion.
Now we only need to consider further the case
when n+1>100, that is, the case when n>99.
But we know n≤100, and thus this is the case
when n=100. Since n=100 and <100,1> < <n,
m>, we also know m>1. Thus we have only to
consider further the case where execution is at
2 with N=n+1=101 and M=m>1. The test N>100
would be true and the test M=1 false, and
hence execution would next proceed from 2 to
3 to 4 to 5 and back to 2. When execution
returns to 2, N=101-10=91 and M=m-1. At that
point the test N>100 would be false, and hence
execution would next proceed from 2 to 6 to 7
and back to 2. When execution returns to 2
we will have N=91+11=102 and M=(m-1)+1=m.
You may verify that execution would continue
in this way to proceed alternately around the
left loop and then the right loop until execution eventually reached point 2 with N=99+11=
110 and M=m. At that point execution would
again proceed arund the left loop and return
to 2 with N=110-10=100 and M=m-1. But <100,
m-1> is in the set X and <100,m-1> < <100,m>.
Thus we may apply the induction hypothesis
and conclude that eventually execution will
return to 2 with N=101 and M=1. This concludes the generalized induction proof that the
assertion attached to 2 is true. Let us now
use this fact to complete the correctness
proof. We only need to consider the case
where the value N_0 read in for N is ≤ 100. In

that case execution first reaches point 2 with $N=N_0 \leqq 100$ and M=1. The assertion attached to 2 tells us that execution will eventually reach 2, with N=101 and M=1. At that point the test N>100 would be true and the test M=1 would also be true, and therefore execution would next proceed from 2 to 3 to 8 to 9 to 10. Thus eventually execution will reach point 10 and when it does the value of N that is printed out will be 101-10=91. This concludes the correctness proof.

It is interesting to compare proofs by inductive assertions to proofs by structural induction for non-recursive (iterative) programs. Proofs by inductive assertions are essentially inductive proofs where the induction is on the number of times execution reaches certain (loops) points in the program. Proofs by structural induction are also inductive proofs, but where the induction is on the structure of the data manipulated by the program. Of course, the structure of the data is usually what determines how many times execution reaches the various points in the program, and thus the two methods are actually quite similar to one another. It just turns out that when the program is essentially recursive in nature and thus makes very explicit use of the structure of the data in determining the flow of control of the program, it is usually easier to prove the correctness of the program using structural induction than it is using inductive assertions. The chief difficulty when using either method is in developing the correct assertions to attach to the loop points in the programs. There is one difference between the type of assertion needed in the two methods. The inductive assertions do not contain any information about termination while the assertions used in structural induction contain information about both partial correctness and termination.

EXERCISES

1. (a) Prove the correctness of the program in Example 4.5.1 by the method of inductive assertions.
    (b) Prove the correctness of the program in

Example 4.5.2 by the method of inductive assertions. This program is particularly difficult to prove correct by the method of inductive assertions and the student should not be surprised if he or she is unable to do so.

2.

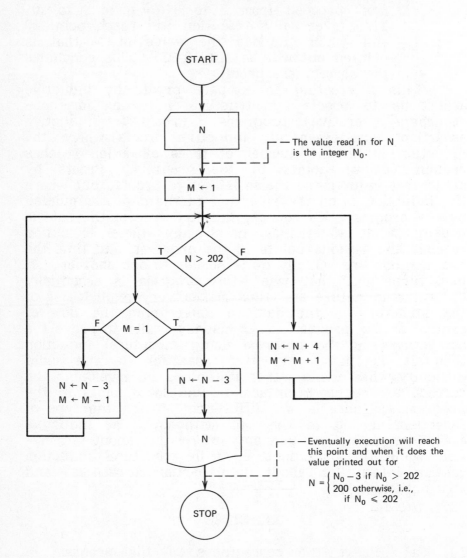

The value read in for N is the integer N_0.

Eventually execution will reach this point and when it does the value printed out for

$$N = \begin{cases} N_0 - 3 & \text{if } N_0 > 202 \\ 200 & \text{otherwise, i.e.,} \\ & \text{if } N_0 \leqslant 202 \end{cases}$$

Prove the correctness of the above program by structural induction.

3.   (a)   Draw a flowchart for preorder traversal of a binary tree and prove it is correct by structural induction (see pages 315-316 of The Art of Computer Programming, Vol. 1, Second Edition, by D. E. Knuth for a definition of preorder and postorder traversal).
      (b)   Draw a flowchart for postorder traversal of a binary tree and prove it is correct by structural induction.

4.

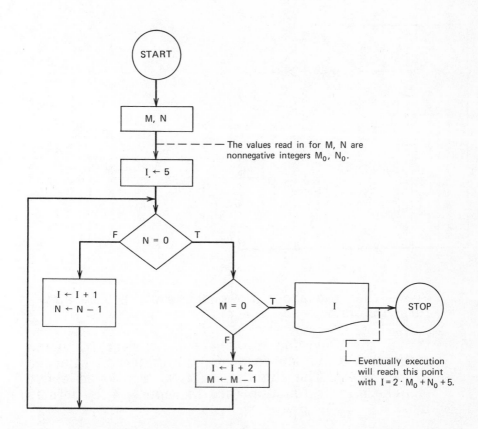

START

M, N

---- The values read in for M, N are nonnegative integers M_0, N_0.

$I \leftarrow 5$

F   N = 0   T

$I \leftarrow I + 1$
$N \leftarrow N - 1$

M = 0   T   I   STOP

F

$I \leftarrow I + 2$
$M \leftarrow M - 1$

Eventually execution will reach this point with $I = 2 \cdot M_0 + N_0 + 5$.

Prove the above flowchart is correct by structural induction and by inductive assertions.

5.

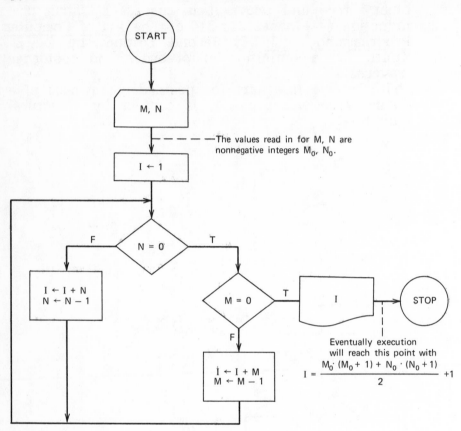

The values read in for M, N are nonnegative integers M_0, N_0.

Eventually execution will reach this point with
$$I = \frac{M_0 \cdot (M_0 + 1) + N_0 \cdot (N_0 + 1)}{2} + 1$$

Prove that the above flowchart is correct by structural induction.

6.   Prove the following flowchart is correct by using structural induction to prove the statement attached to point 2.   The function A(M,N) mentioned above is Ackermann's function (see Example 4.4.2) defined by

A(X1,X2) ≡ IF X1 = 0 THEN X2 + 1

ELSE IF X2 = 0 THEN A(X1-1,1)

ELSE OTHERWISE A(X1-1,A(X1,X2-1))

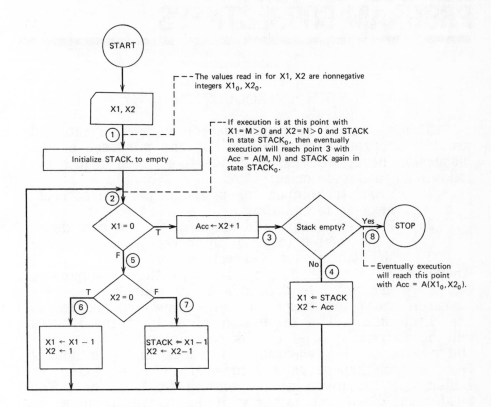

CHAPTER FIVE

CURRENT RESEARCH RELATED TO PROVING PROGRAM CORRECTNESS

5.1 INTRODUCTION

There is much current research in areas related to proving program correctness. For the purposes of the discussion here, we wish to divide this research into the following broad categories:
1.   Proof techniques for proving (partial) correctness or termination,
2.   Program design and language design considerations related to program correctness.
3.   Mechanization of correctness proofs.
There is substantial overlap between these categories, and they are not intended to sharply delineate separate research areas but merely to give some organization to the discussion. The discussion of each of these areas will be extremely brief and is only intended to suggest the nature of the research in the area and point out a few research papers related to each area. An extensive bibliography is given at the end of this chapter. The reader could use it together with the references given in each section to pursue any of these areas in depth.

5.2 PROOF TECHNIQUES

In this text, we have concentrated on two basic proof techniques, the method of inductive assertions and the technique of structural induction. The method of inductive assertions was first presented in Floyd (1967) and Naur (1966). The technique of structural induction was first presented in Burstall (1969). In Section 3.4 we also briefly introduced the notion of verification rules or axioms for proving partial correctness. This technique was first presented in Hoare (1969).

There have been a number of other proof techniques suggested for proving program correctness. Manna, Pnueli (1970, 1974), Burstall (1974), Basu, Yeh (1975), Dijkstra (1976) and Katz, Manna (1976) all contain different proof techniques for proving the total correctness of iterative programs. Landin, Burstall (1969) gives a rather different, algebraic approach to correctness proofs. Burstall (1972) and Wegbreit, Spitzer (1975) disucss techniques for proving the correctness of programs that use complex data structures or modify their data structures. Manna (1970C) shows how to use the method of inductive assertions to prove the correctness of nondeterministic programs. Lipton (1975), Ashcroft (1975), Owicki, Gries (1976), and Keller (1976) discuss methods of proving the correctness of parallel programs.

Proof techniques such as inductive assertions that only prove partial correctness require a separate proof of termination. A number of techniques have been suggested for proving the termination of iterative programs. Floyd (1967) and Manna (1970) investigate the use of well-ordered (or well-founded) sets for proving termination. Manna (1975) discusses and compares several different methods for proving termination. Sites (1974) discusses techniques for proving that programs terminate cleanly.

Many inductive methods have been presented for proving the correctness of recursive programs. McCarthy (1963), DeBaker, Scott (1969), Park (1969), and Morris (1971) all present slightly different inductive methods in which the induction is on the level of recursion. These differ from proofs by structural induction as presented in this book, where the induction is on the structure of the data manipulated by the program. Manna, Ness, Vuillemin (1973) discuss and compare many of these different inductive methods for proving the correctness of recursive programs.

The book by Manna (1974) gives a somewhat formal treatement of many of the known techniques for proving program correctness; Chapter 2 treats methods for proving the correctness and termination of iterative programs while Chapter 5 does the same for recursive programs.

5.3   PROGRAM DESIGN -- LANGUAGE DESIGN

The desire to produce programs that are easier to verify has had a considerable effect upon program design and language design. Dijkstra (1968a) was one of the first papers to relate program design and verification. Similarly, Dijkstra (1968b) was one of the first papers to relate a language design consideration (namely, the elimination of the GO TO statement) to correctness considerations. Naur (1969) is also a very early paper relating program design and verification.

Much of the recent work relating program design to correctness considerations goes under the rubric of structured programming. The emphasis in this area is on design techniques that allow the programmer to see (informally verify) that the program is correct at each stage of the programming process. Dahl, Dijkstra, Hoare (1972) and McGowan, Kelly (1975) are two books that treat this topic. Wirth (1973) is a beginning programming text that also treats structured programming and correctness proofs. Hoare (1972b) gives a detailed correctness proof for a structured program. Mills (1971a, b, 1975) and Baker (1975) are powerful advocates of structured programming in a production programming environment. Knuth (1974) discusses structured programming and the use of GO TO statements.

Starting with Dijkstra's attack on the GO TO statement, there have been many papers reflecting the influence of correctness consideration on programming language design. Among the programming languages that have been influenced by correctness considerations are Pascal (Wirth 1971), Alphard (Wulf 1974), Clu (Liskov, Zilles 1974), and Nucleus (Good, Ragland 1973, Good 1974). Hoare (1971a) discussed possible restrictions on procedures and parameters in order to facilitate correctness proofs. Morriss (1972) discusses verification-oriented language design. Clark (1977) discusses programming language constructs for which it is impossible to obtain good Hoares like axiom systems. He shows that if a programming language contains certain common features then it is impossible to obtain a sound and complete Hoare-like axiom system for the language. He suggests that such features should be modified or eliminated from the language in order to facilitate correctness proofs.

The recent book by Dijkstra (1976) is relevant to both of the topics of this and the preceeding section. This book presents a new formalism for carrying out correctness proofs and a new (mini) programming language that is used for all of the programming examples in the book. The programming language was specifically designed to contain only very simple yet powerful programming constructs that lend themselves to the verification technique used in the book. The bulk of the book then consists of a series of programs for which the author presents detailed design and verification considerations.

5.4   MECHANIZATION OF CORRECTNESS PROOFS

Much of the research in the area of proving programs correct is aimed at formalizing and ultimately mechanizing such proofs. If workable mechanical verification systems can be produced they will represent a tremendous step forward in computing science. Although informal correctness proofs of the type discussed in this book are valuable, they are subject to many errors. It would be a great advantage to have a mechanical verification system that could interactively aid in the attempted correctness proof and serve as an infallible proof checker. The extent to which this goal will prove feasable remains to be seen. There do already exist, however, several first attempts at building such systems.

If we wish to use mechanical verification systems to help with correctness proofs then the inductive assertions and proofs will have to be formalized in some way. Most often they have been formalized in the symbolism of the first-order predicate calculus, although this is in some ways an unsuitable formalism for stating the assertions and proofs. Burstall (1970) and chapter 2 of Manna's book (1974) contain examples of correctness proofs formalized in the notation of the first-order predicate calculus. Liskov, Zilles (1975) investigates various specification tedchniques that could be used for formally stating the inductive assertions.

Most of the mechanical verification systems that

168 Current Research Related to Proving Correctness

have actually been built are based on the inductive assertions method. These mechanical verification systems take as input the source program to be verified together with programmer supplied inductive assertions. Based on built-in knowledge of the syntax and semantics of the programming language, the systems trace out all control paths through the program and generate the set of verification conditions that must be proved to verify the program. Section 2.6 illustrated how such formalized verification conditions can be generated. The systems then attempt to prove the verification conditions by means of algebraic and Boolean simplification routines and a first-order predicate claculus theorem prover. Because the mechanical theorem proving routines are likely to fail on at least some of the proofs, the systems are usually interactive and allow the user to provide help on the portions of the proofs that have failed. King (1969, 1971), Deutsch (1973), Good, London, Bledsoe (1975), and Suzuki (1975) describe implemented mechanical verification systems of the type discussed above. Cooper (1971), Elspas, Levitt, Waldinger (1971), Igarashi, London, Luckham (1973), and Waldinger, Levitt (1974) also discuss mechanical verification systems.

Boyer, Moore (1973) describes an implemented mechanical verification system for proving theorems about LISP programs. It differs substantially from the systems described above. Since it is designed to prove theorems about recursively defined programs, it uses structural induction as the underlying method rather than inductive assertions.

All of the mechanical verification systems that use the method of inductive assertions require the user to supply the inductive assertions. It would be extremely helpful if the system itself could devise some or all of the inductive assertions. Caplin (1975), Greif, Waldinger (1974), Wegbreit (1974), German, Wegbreit (1975), and Katz, Manna (1976) describe various heuristic methods for attempting to mechanically generate inductive assertions. While none of these methods works for all programs, some combination of such methods may form a useful aid for generating many of the routine inductive assertions.

Some of the ideas and techniques of mechanical verification systems are also being used in more limited systems that are designed to help the programmer systematically test and debug the program. King (1975, 1976), and Boyer, Elspas, Levitt (1975) describe implemented systems of this type.

DESCRIPTOR-INDEXED BIBLIOGRAPHY

In the following bibliography we have attempted to classify each reference according to its subject material. We have used the following descriptors for the classification:

PC Techniques for proving correctness or examples of such proofs.
PCR Techniques for proving correctness of recursive programs or examples of such proofs.
PT Techniques for proving termination.
D   Program design methods whose aim is to produce a verifiable program.
L   Programming language considerations related to proving correctness.
M   Mechanization of correctness proofs. (Semi) Automatic verification systems.
F   Formalization of correctness proofs.
A   Automatic theorem proving methods used in (semi) automatic verification systems.
H   Heuristic methods for generating inductive assertions.
T   Program test methods related to techniques for proving correctness.
G   General, containing material concerning many of the above topics.

This classification follows along the lines of the categories used in the discussion in Chapter 5. It is both arbitrary and overlapping but hopefully will provide at least some guidance for the reader interested in a specific subject. We have attempted to give a substantial and representative selection of references to material related to proving program correctness. However, we

170

have not even attempted to make this a complete bibliography of all known references related to that subject. We have listed only a few particularly important references published before 1970. London (1970c) is an extensive bibliography of such papers published prior to 1970.

Ashcroft, E., and Z. Manna (1971): "The Translation of 'GO TO' Programs to 'WHILE' Programs," Proc. IFIP Cong., North-Holland Publ. Co., Amsterdam, 1971, pp. 250-255.
    D, L

Baker, F. T. (1975): "Structured Programming in a Production Programming Envioronment," Proc. Int. Con. on Reliable Software, Los Angeles, April 21-23, 1975, pp. 172-185.
    D

Basu, S. K., and J. Misra (1975): "Proving Loop Programs," IEEE Trans. on Software Engineering, vol. Se-1, No. 1, March 1975, pp. 76-86.
    PC, F

Basu, S. K., and R. T. Yeh (1975): "Strong Verification of Programs," IEEE Trans. on Software Engineering, Vol. SE-1, No. 3, September 1975, pp. 339-345.
    PC, F

Boyer, R. S., and J. S. More (1975): "Proving Theorems about Lisp Functions," J. ACM, 22 (1), January 1975, pp. 129-144.
    M

Burstall, R. M. (1969): "Proving Properties of Programs by Structural Induction," Comput. J., 12, 1969, pp. 41-48.
    PCR, PT

Burstall, R. M., and P. J. Landin (1969): "Programs and their Proofs: An Algebraic Approach," Machine Intelligence, 4, B. Meltzer, and D. Michie (Eds.), Edinburgh University Press, 1969, pp. 17-43.
    PC, PT

Burstall, R. M. (1970): "Formal Description of Program Structure and Semantics in First-order logic," Machine Intelligence, 5, B. Meltzer and D. Michie (Eds.) Edinburg University Press, 1970, pp. 79-98.
    PC, F

Burstall, R. M. (1972): "Some Techniques for Proving Correctness of Programs Which alter Data Structures," Machine Intelligence, 7, D. Michie (Ed.), American Elsevier, New York, 1972, pp.
    PC

Burstall, R. M. (1974): "Program Proving as Hand Simulation with a Little Induction," Information Processing, 74, Proceedings of IFIP Congress 74, J. L. Rosenfeld (Ed.), North-Holland, 1974, pp. 308-312.
    PC, PT

Caplain, M. (1975): "Finding Invariant Assertions For Proving Programs," Proc. Int. Conf. on Reliable Software, Los Angeles, April 1975, pp. 165-171.
    H

Chang, C-L., R. C-T. Lee (1973): Symbolic Logic and Mechanical Theorem Proving, Academic Press, 1973.
    A

Clark, E. M. (1977): "Programming Language Con-structs for Which it is Impossible to Obtain Good Hoare-Like Axiom Systems," Conference Record of the Fourth ACM Symposium on Principles of Programming Languages, Los Angeles, January 17-19, 1977, pp. 10-17.
    L

Clint, M. (1973): "Program Proving: Coroutines," Acta Informatica, pp. 50-63.
    PC

Clint, M., and C. A. Hoare (1972): "Program Proving: Jumps and Functions," Acta Informatica, 1(3), 1972, pp. 214-224.
    PC, F

Cooper, D. C. (1971): "Programs for Mechanical Program Verification," Machine Intelligence, 6, B. Meltzer and D. Michie (Eds.) Edinburgh University Press, 1972, pp. 43-59.
    M

Dahl, O. J., E. W. Dijkstra, and C. A. R. Hoare (1972): Structured Programming, Academic Press, London, 1972.
    D

DeBakker, J. W. (1971): Recursive Procedures, Mathematical Center, Amsterdam, Holland, 1971.
    PCR

Deutsch, L. P. (1973): "An Interactive Program Verifier," Ph.D. thesis, University of California, Berkeley, 1973. Also Xerox Palo Alto Research Center Report CSL-73-1, May 1973.
    M

Dijkstra, E. W. (1968a): "A Constructive Approach to the Problem of Program Correctness," B.I.T., 8, 1968, pp. 174-186.
    D

Dijkstra, E. W. (1968b): "Goto Statement Considered Harmful," Letter to Editor, C. ACM, 11, (1968), pp. 147-148. Reply, Comm. ACM, 11, 1968, pp. 538-541.
    D, L

Dijkstra, W. E. (1968c): "The Structure of the 'THE' Multiprogramming System," Comm. ACM, 11, 1968, pp. 341-346.
    D

Dijkstra, E. W. (1975): "Guarded Commands, Nondeterminancy and Formal Derivation of Programs," Comm. ACM, 18, August 1975, pp. 453-457.
    D, F

Dijkstra, E. W. (1976): A Discipline of Programming, Prentice-Hall, Englewood Cliffs, N.J., 1976.
    PC, PT, D, L, F

Elspas, B. (1974): "The Semiautomatic Generation of Inductive Assertions for Proving Program Correctness," Stanford Research Institute Project 2686 Interim Report, July 1974.
    H

Elspas, B., K. N. Levitt, and R. J. Waldinger (1973): "An Interactive System for the Verification of Computer Programs," Stanford Research Institute Project 1891 Final Report, September 1973.
    M

Elspas, B., K. N. Levitt, R. J. Waldinger, and A. Waksman (1972): "An Assessment of Techniques for Proving Program Correctness," ACM Computing Surveys, 4, (2), June 1972, pp. 97-147.
    PC, PT, M

Floyd, R. W. (1967): "Assigning Meanings to Programs," Proc. Symp. Appl. Math., Vol. 19: Mathematical Aspects of Computer Science, J. T. Schwartz (Ed.), American Mathematical Society, Providence, R.I., 1967, pp. 19-32.
    PC, PT

German, S. M. and B. Wegbreit (1975): "A synthesizer of Inductive Assertions," AFIPS Conference Proceedings, Vol. 44, 1975 National Computer Conference, AFIPS Press.
    H

Goldstine, H. H., and J. von Neumann (1963): Planning and Coding Problems for an Electronic Computer Instrument," John von Neumann, Collected Works, 5, A. H. Taub (Ed.), Pergamon Press, New York, 1963, pp. 80-235 (see especially p. 92 for the use of an assertion box).
    PC

Good, D. I. (1970): "Toward a Man-Machine System for Proving Program Correctness," Ph.D. thesis, University of Wisconsin, June 1970.
    M

Good, D. I., and L. C. Ragland (1973): "Nucleus -- A language of Provable Programs," Program Test Methods, W. C. Hetzel (Ed.), Prentice-Hall, 1973, pp. 93-117.
    L

Good, D. I., R. L. London, and W. W. Bledsoe (1975): "An Interactive Program Verification System" IEEE Transactions on Software Engineering, 1(1), April 1975, pp. 59-67.
    M

Green, C. (1969): "The Application of Theorem Proving to Question-Answer Systems," Ph.D. thesis, Computer Science Department, Stanford University, 1969.
    A

Greif, I., and R. A. Waldinger (1974): "A More Mechanical Heuristic Approach to Program Verification," Proc. Int. Symp. on Programming, Paris, April 1974, pp. 83-90.
    H

Hantler, S. C., and J. C. King (1976): "An Introduction to Proving the Correctness of Programs," ACM Computing Surveys, September 1976, pp. 331-353.
    PC

von Henke, F. W., and D. C. Luckham (1975): "A Methodology for Verifying Programs," Proc. Int. Conf. on Reliable Software, Los Angeles, April 21-23, 1975.
    M

Hoare, C. A. R. (1969): "An Axiomatic Basis of Computer Programming," Comm. ACM, 12 (10), October 1969, pp. 576-583.
    PC, F

Hoare, C. A. R. (1971a): "Procedures and Parameters: An Axiomatic Approach," Symposium on Semantics of

Algorithmic Languages, E. Engler (Ed.) Springer-Verlag, 1971, pp. 102-116.
    PC, L

Hoare, C. A. R. (1971b): "Proof of a Program: FIND," Comm. ACM, 14 (1), January 1971, pp. 39-45.
    PC

Hoare, C. A. R. (1972a): "Proof of correctness of Data Representations," Acta Informatica, 1(4), 1972, pp. 271-281.
    PC

Hoare, C. A. R. (1972b): "Proof of a Structured Program: 'The Sieve of Eratosthenes'," Computer J., 15 (4), 1972, pp. 321-325.
    PC, D

Hoare, C. A. R., (1973): "A Structured Paging System," Computer J., 16 (3), August 1973, pp. 209 -215.
    D

Howden, W. E. (1976): "Symbolic Testing and the DISSECT Symbolic Evaluation System," Tech. Report No. 11, Department of Applied Physics and Information Science, University of California, San Diego, May 1976.
    T

Huang, J. C. (1976): "A Method for Program Analysis and its Applications to Program-Correctness Problems," Int. J. of Computer Mathematics, 5, (4), 1976, pp. 203-227.
    PC, F

Hull, T. E., W. H. Enright, and A. E. Sedgwick (1972): "The Correctness of Numerical Algorithms," Proc. ACM Conference on Proving Assertions About Programs, SIGPLAN Notices, 7(1), 1972, pp. 66-73.
    PC

Igarashi, S., R. L. London, and D. C. Luckham, (1973): "Automatic Program Verification I: A Logical Basis and

Its Implementation," ACTA Informatica, 4, 1973, pp. 145-182.
    M

Kaplan, D. M. (1969): "Recursion Induction Applied to Generalized Flowcharts," Proc. 24th Nat. Ass. Comput. Mach. Conf., pp. 491-504. ACM, New York, 1969.
    PCR

Katz, S., and Z. Manna (1975): "A Closer Look at Termination," Acta Informatica 1975, pp. 333-352
    PT

Katz, S., and Z. Manna (1976): "Logical Analysis of Programs," Comm. ACM, 19, (4), April 1976, pp. 188-206.
    PC, PT, H

King, J. C. (1969): "A Program Verifier," Ph.D. thesis, Carnegie-Mellon University, 1969.
    M

King, J. C., and R. W. Floyd, (1970): "An Interpretation Oriented Theorem Prover Over Integers," Proc. 2nd Annual ACM Symposium on Theory of Computing, ACM, New York, 1970, pp. 169-179.
    A

King, J. C. (1971): "Proving Programs to be Correct," IEEE Transactions on Computers, 11, November 1971, pp. 1331-1336.
    M

King, J. C. (1975): "A New Approach to Program Testing," Proc. Int. Conf. on Reliable Software, Los Angeles, April 21-23, 1975, pp. 228-233. Also appears in Programming Methodology, Lecture Notes in Computer Science, 23, Springer-Verlag, New York, 1971, pp. 278-290.
    T

King, J. C. (1976): "Symbolic Execution and Program Testing," Comm. ACM 19 (7), July 1976, pp. 385-394.
    T

Keller, R. M. (1976): "Formal Verification of Parallel Programs," Comm. ACM, July 1976, pp. 371-384.
   PC

Knuth, D. E. (1974): "Structured Programming with go to Statements," ACM Computing Surveys, 6 (4), December 1974, pp. 261-302.
   D, L

Lipton, R. J. (1975): "Reduction: A Method of Proving Properties of Parallel Programs," Comm. ACM, December 1975, pp. 717-721.
   PC

Liskov, B. H., and S. Zilles (1974): "Programming with Abstract Data Types," Proceedings of ACM SIGPLAN Conference on Very High Level Languages, SIGPLAN Notices, 9 (3), April 1974, pp. 50-59.
   L

London, R. L. (1970a): "Proving Programs Correct: Some Techniques and Examples," BIT, 10, 1970, pp. 168-182.
   PC, PT

London, R. L. (1970b): "Proof of Algorithms: A New Kind of Certification." Comm. ACM, 13(6), 1970, pp. 371-373.

London, R. L. (1970c): "Bibliography on Proving the Correctness of Computer Programs," Machine Intelligence, 5, B. Meltzer and D. Michie (Eds.), American Elsevier Publ. Co., New York. 1970, pp. 569-580.
   G

London, R. L. (1972): "Correctness of a Compiler for a LISP Subset," Proc. ACM Conference on Proving Assertions about Programs, SIGPLAN Notices, 7(1), 1972, pp. 121-127. Full proofs in correctness of two compilers for a Lisp subset, Stanford University Artificial Intelligence Laboratory Memo 151, October 1971.
   PC

London, R. L., "A View of Program Verification," Proc. Int. Con. on Reliable Software, Los Angeles, April 21-23, 1975, pp. 534-545.
G

Manna, Z. (1969): "Properties of Programs and First-Order Predicate Calculus," J. ACM, 16(2), April 1969, pp. 244-255.
PC, PT, F

Manna, Z. (1970): "The Correctness of Non-Deterministic Programs," Artificial Intelligence, An International Journal, 1(1), 1970, pp. 1-26.
PC, F

Manna, Z., and J. McCarthy (1970): "Properties of Programs and Partial Function Logic," Machine Intelligence, 5, B. Meltzer and D. Mitchie (Eds.), American Elsevier Publ. Co., New York, 1970, pp. 27-37.
PCR, PT

Manna, Z., and A. Pnueli (1970): "Formalization of Properties of Functional Programs," J. ACM, 17(3), 1970, pp. 555-569.
PC

Manna, Z., and J. Vuillemin (1972): "Fixpoint Approach to the Theory of Computation," Comm. ACM, 15(7), 1972, pp. 528-536.
PCR

Manna, Z., S. Ness, and J. Vuillemin (1973): "Inductive Methods for Proving Properties of Programs," Comm. ACM, 16(8), August 1973, pp. 491-502.
PCR

Manna, Z. (1974): Mathematical Theory of Computation, McGraw-Hill, New York, 1974.
PC, PT, F

McCarthy, J. (1963): "A Basis for a Mathematical Theory of Computation," Computer Programming and Formal Systems, P. Braffort and D. Hirschberg (Eds.)

North Holland, Amsterdam 1963, pp. 33-70. Also Proceedings of th Western Join Computer Conference, Spartan Books, New York, 1961, pp. 225-238.
    PC, PT

McCarthy, J., and J. A. Painter, (1967): "Correctness of a Compiler for Arithmetic Expressions," Proceedings of a Symposium in Applied Mathematic, Vol. 19, Mathematical Aspects of Computer Science, J. T. Schwartz, (Ed.), American Mathematical Society, Providence, Rhode Island, 1967, pp. 33-41.
    PC

McGowan, C. L., and J. R. Kelly, (1975): "Top Down Structured Programming Techniques," Petrocelli/Charter, New York, 1975.
    D

Marmier, E. (1974): "A Program Verifier for Pascal," Information Processing 74, Proceedings of IFIP Congress 74, J. L. Rosefeld (Ed.), North-Holland, 1974, pp. 177-181.
    M

Mills, H. D. (1971a): "Top-down Programming in Large Systems," In: Debugging Techniques in Large Systems, Randal Rustin (Ed.), Prentice-Hall, Englewood Cliffs, N.J., 1971, pp. 41-55.
    D

Mills, H. D. (1971b): "The New Math of Computer Programming," Comm. ACM, 18(1), January 1975, pp. 43-48.
    D

Mills, H. D. (1975): "How to Write Correct Programs and Know It," Proceedings of the International Conference on Reliable Software, Los Angeles, April 21-23, 1975, pp. 363-370.
    D

Morris, J. H. (1968): "Another Recursion Induction Principle," Comm. ACM, 14(5), pp. 351-354.
    PCR

Morris, J. H., Jr. (1972): "Verification-Oriented Language Design," University of California, Berkeley, Computer Science Technical Report 7, 1972.
    L

Naur, P. (1966): "Proof of Algorithms by General Snapshots," B.I.T., 6, 1966, pp. 310-316.
    PC

Naur, P. (1969): "Programming by Action Clusters," B.I.T., 9(3), 1969, pp. 250-258.
    D

Oppen, D. C., and S. A. Cook (1975: "Proving Assertions About Programs that Manipulate Data Structures," Seventh Annual ACM Symposium on Theory of Computation, 1975, ACM, New York, pp. 107-116.
    PC

Park, D. (1969): "Fixpoint Induction and Proofs of Program Properties," Machine Intelligence, 5, B. Meltzer, and D. Michie (Eds.), American Elsevier Publ. Co., New York, 1969, pp. 59-78.
    PCR

Scott, D. (1970): "Outline of a Mathematical Theory of Computation," 4th Annu. Princeton Conf. Inform. Sciences and Syst., 1970, pp. 169-176.
    PCR

Sites, R. L. (1974): "Proving that Computer Programs Terminate Cleanly," Ph.D. thesis, Stanford University, 1974. Also Computer Science Report STAN-CS-74-418, May 1974.
    PT

Suzuki, N. (1975): "Verifying Programs by Algebraic and Logical Reduction," Proc. Int. Conf. on Reliable Software, Los Angeles, April 21-23, 1975, pp. 478-481.
    M

Waldinger, R., and K. N. Levitt, (1974): Reasoning about Programs," Artificial Intelligence, 5, B. Meltzer and D. Michie (Eds.), 1974, pp. 235-316.
    M

Wegbreit, B. (1970): "The Synthesis of Loop Predicates," Comm. ACM, 17(2), February 1974, pp. 102-112.
    H

Wegbreit, B. (1975a): "Property Extraction in Well-Founded Property Sets," IEEE Trans on Software Engineering, Vol. SE-1, No. 3, September 1975, pp. 270-285.
    H

Wegbreit, B. (1975b): "Mechanical Program Analysis," Comm. ACM, 18(9), September 1975, pp. 528-539.
    PC

Wegbreit B., and J. M. Spitzen, (1976): "Proving Properties of Complex Data Structures," J. ACM, 23(2), April 1976, pp. 389-396.
    PC

Wirth, N. (1973): Systematic Programming: An Introduction, Prentice-Hall, Englewood Cliffs, N.J., 1973.
    PC, PT, D

Wirth, N. (1974): "On the Composition of Well-Structured Programs," ACM Computing Surveys, 6,(4), December 1974, pp. 247-260.
    D

Wulf, W. A. (1974): "Alphard: Toward a Language to Support Structured Programs," Carnegie-Mellon University Computer Science report, April 1974.
    L

INDEX